BEGUILED BY A WILD THING

Beguiled by a Wild Thing

Reflex Fiction
Volume Four

REFLEX PRESS

First published as a collection in 2021 by Reflex Press
Abingdon, Oxfordshire, OX14 3SY
www.reflex.press

ISBN: 978-1-914114-05-2

1 3 5 7 9 10 8 6 4 2

Printed and bound in Great Britain
by Imprint Digital

Cover image by Nadia Grapes/Shutterstock

www.reflex.press/beguiled-by-a-wild-thing/

CONTENTS

FOREWORD

This anthology brings the curtain down on the fourth year of the Reflex flash fiction competition. Who would have thought on the 1st December 2019, when the spring contest opened, that in just a few months, we'd be in the grip of a global pandemic? It's been a difficult time for everyone, and we thank all our readers and writers for continuing to support Reflex. In turn, we hope we've been able to bring some relief from world events with our regular competitions and daily stories on our website.

~

Congratulations to all 142 authors who feature in this anthology. The quality of entries we receive at Reflex is phenomenal, and just making the longlist of 50 is a significant achievement. A special mention for our four winners, 'Good for Her' by D Brody Lipton, 'Mouse' by Gillian O'Shaughnessy, 'Failure to Engage' by Kali Richmond, and 'How Red and Black Fade to Grey' by Faye Brinsmead. This year the title story and inspiration for the cover, 'Beguiled by a Wild Thing', comes from Danielle Baldock.

We would like to thank our guest judges, Tania Hershman, David Gaffney, Stephanie Carty, and Kathy Fish, and our team of volunteer readers coordinated by Katy Hill.

David Borrowdale
Publisher, Reflex Press
May 2021

How Red and Black Fade to Grey
Faye Brinsmead
SPRING 2020 FIRST PLACE

You can't trust night anymore. It's just day, but blacker, a toxic film coating our bodies, licking its way into our lungs. I lie in bed spitting cinders, making up stories I can't write.

On windy days, we ran through the bush catching leaves in our mouths.

How it could start. Catching leaves catching fire. Twenty-five million acres. Bigger than Austria and Azerbaijan stitched together with red thread.

Once, I swallowed a gum nut. A fibrous mass swelled in my gut, took over my body. Twigs burst through my skin; sap burbled in my alveoli.

Allergic reaction to bushfire smoke, the doctor says. Bronchospasms, phoney asthma. I'll put you on Ventolin.

Koalas sheltered in my ears.

Viral images of cuteness in distress. Bedraggled blobs bailing up cyclists, climbing tyres like trees to beg for water. Coming out in a rainbow rash of knitted mittens. What about the uncute ones? Would you knit a tail-protector for a snake?

Moths scribbled memoirs on my trunk.

Seven hundred insect species gone, maybe more. Ones we hadn't discovered. A ghost host of unknown unknowns.

I was an ecosystem. We thrummed and twittered, shed our bark, snaked our roots.

We gasp and choke. We, crouched inside our reverse cycle air conditioners with our HEPA filters and our P2 masks. Trees can't hide.

On windy days, we ran through the catching in our mouths.

If a great forgetting falls on us.

Once, I swallowed.

If we stop saying their names.

Sheltered in my ears.

Misplacing pieces, day by day.

Scribbled memoirs on my.

Lost in the forever grey of environmental dementia.

I was an.

Get Gone

Tania Hershman

SPRING 2020 SECOND PLACE

Get gone, girl, she snarls, and the girl, who never knows what she might be getting, goes. Galloping across roads, the girl feels herself small, feels herself dissolving. Giant clouds at the level of her shoulders try to make her laugh, but the girl is not amused. Get gone, she herself says to the clouds, and to the snails that line the way, watching. Girls and snails never mix, this she knew from early on.

Gathered in to herself later, after a day or week, she sits, fed and small and almost but not dissolved. Girls so easily disappear, she lost several, and has had to keep herself withstanding. Gently, says a voice from besides, and the girl does not need to turn to know it is the one who often comes at this point. Gentle, she says to the voice, is not how I am feeling. Get yourself there, says the one who has no body. Go away, all of you, telling me what, where and how. Good, whispers the voice, so soft the girl almost unhears it. Good for you, girl.

Girls later become not-girls, and how they are then depends some on how they were spoken to, and some on how they choose to allow themselves to speak and be spoken of. Gone are the days of girls mapping onto just one way, and our girl knows that where there is a fork, she must decide. Growling softly, our girl, who has grown much further from the snails, much closer to the clouds, meanders up to that first roadway split.

Give me an indication, she asks the clouds, but they who had tried to amuse her now are uninterested. Give me some help, she says to the snails, but they make as if they can't hear her. Glancing down one way then down the other way, our girl puts out her foot, withdraws, turns then turns again. Get gone, girl, she says to herself, takes a step and another step and there she is, we can see her striding, we watch her leap away. Good, we say. Good for you, girl.

Coyote Tooth
Avra Margariti
SPRING 2020 THIRD PLACE

My stepmother Christine is six months younger than me. She lives in a trailer park in the desert, where she does palm readings for a fiver and collects strange animal remains to use in charms and divinations. I always stay with her the weekend closest to my father's death anniversary.

'Sadie, you'll live much longer than he did,' she tells me, tracing a line across my palm. It's caked with mud since I helped her look for a coyote tooth earlier.

'What about love?' I ask. 'Will I love better than him?'

My stepmother Christine doesn't know.

I ask if I can read her palm, and she lets me, though I don't have the gift. Our hands fit together like warm apostrophes. I poke the bumps of her knuckles until I reach the last one. My stepmother Christine is missing half a finger. *Did you break a pinky promise?* I asked her once, back when I thought of her as my father's revenge on my mother and I.

She chuckled with her earthy timbre. 'Oh, no, love. I lost my finger long ago. It was bitten off by a starving animal while I was trying to feed it.'

And yet, she kept on loving wild beasts. She must have, considering she married my father.

In the peace-quilted night, stars wheel above the desertscape. We sit outside on crooked lawn chairs and drink homemade beer out of pickle jars. I don't want to celebrate my father's memory, but my stepmother Christine insists we must. He wanted us to be enemies. The fact that we're here together is fuck-you enough, so I splash some honey droplets skyward and pour the rest of my beer into the cracked earth. A tribute to my father, but mostly a way to appease her.

My stepmother Christine beams at me, gentle as the smile she reserves for dead animals, and I feel seen and precious like a coyote tooth atop her palmistry table.

Then It Was Autumn Again
Sherri Turner

In Paris, they don't catch falling leaves in autumn like people in England do. Well, the people outside the shop on the Boulevard Haussmann certainly didn't. They looked at us as though we were mad, dancing under the branches, our arms flailing. 'Les Anglais – fous!' we heard them say.

I don't know how they knew we were English, our involuntary outpourings as we leapt and twirled unintelligible as a language. We didn't care. We were indeed mad – mad with love, leaping and twirling at the joy of it.

We drank pastis from tiny glasses and cafe-au-lait from oversized cups, crammed croissants into our mouths, into each other's mouths. We walked along the banks of the Seine where the gay couples sunbathe and let them check you out, although it was clear you were taken. We threw coins from bridges to ensure our return and spent afternoons in bed with the sounds of Paris a backdrop to our passion.

Back in England, it couldn't go on. There were bills and jobs, and you forgot who we had been in Paris. I told you we were still those people, but you couldn't see it. The winter brought a sharp chill that didn't thaw through spring and summer, and then it was autumn again.

I bought fresh croissants, pastis, tiny glasses and took them to your office, just to be mad again. I poured two shots and waited on a bench outside. There was a girl there, laughing and shouting in French as she ran among the trees that edged the car park, trying to catch a leaf.

The glasses slipped from my hand and shattered on the tarmac as I remembered that I'd never seen anyone do that in France and realised that someone must have taught her.

Post Partum
Louise Rimmer

I can lie here on the grass all day if I want to. There is no schedule. I have been demoted to childhood. My mind is empty. I feel like gold-topped milk, dogeared storybooks and ignorant, hairless skin.

The insect and I are playing a game. Butterflies don't usually land on people. They tend to cower, hopping nervously from laceflower to lily of the valley, before taking flight and disappearing forever. But this one is confident and foolish. She jumps onto my right hand, then flutters above me before landing on my left. My sinister hand. I can almost hear her giggle with joy. She sounds like my Ivy-Belle.

The butterfly floats down to the grass to spread her wings. She reveals her patterns to me. Fuzzy circles, two spiral eyes, hypnotised. I think again of Ivy-Belle. I wonder where my daughter is. Maybe she is in the kitchen, with her dad. Or has she crawled to the edge of the garden, where she shouldn't be? There are things that babies should not meddle with.

The grass scratches me as I rise. Its tiny claws rest between my toes. The doctors say that I need to walk slowly. The scar might tear. I have had enough of the game, but the butterfly follows me. She tickles my naked shoulder. It is irritating, like a minuscule electric shock. I flap, trying not to injure her, but she is insistent.

I'm not playing anymore, I scream. She persists by creating a tiny breeze with her wings. Her presence is huge. She suffocates me. My wounds throb. My pain is her fault.

I swat her with a swift backhand, as my father used to. The butterfly releases a squeal, falls, twitches. I have torn her wing, I think, satisfied. I am impatient now. My brow burns under the white watercolour sun. I stamp on the butterfly. It takes multiple blows, as my feet are bare, but eventually she stops moving.

I hear a descant choir of steel kitchen utensils dropping to the floor. My husband hooks under my armpits, disabling me. I can't play anymore, I scream. My wound rips open, again.

Alice Paints Her Kitchen Blue
Olivia Kingery

Alice looks up the etymology for blue and doesn't agree that every-thing blue is cold.

She does the painting at night, turns on the TV, mutes it, turns up the heat, calls her mother. She plays Monopoly by herself within the blue walls and cries when she loses. There is paint on the ceiling, re-frigerator, living room couch, on the silverware. Everything is blue, and only she is cold.

Alice mainly cooks thick slabs of bacon until crisp, cracking yolky eggs with one hand onto the grease, all the while thinking of blue. She thinks of being a boy, how blue means you, when you is a *y* chro-mosome, two open arms, reaching into the blue sky.

When Alice has people over for dinner, she finds them staring at the blue walls in her kitchen too. At the sink she catches them rubbing their index fingers against the white trim, finding the space where blue and white meet. They explore the place where heat has pulled the paint back, separating from itself, running from itself. They explore the place where blue opens up and invites you in.

Alice thinks back to etymology, about the color of the sky, of a new bruise, of an opening mouth – about being a girl, and how it is much like being a bruise. Blue seems so far away, deep in a space her eyes can never fully reach. She tries. She thinks to herself, *I like being cold anyway*.

Florence Owens Thompson, Migrant Mother 1936
Shannon Savvas

Joanna sips her coffee from a gilt-edged Villeroy & Boch mug; racing green, like the electric Jaguar SUV Anthony had bought her for the weekend run to Chalford Hill. She's been told mugs are more egalitarian than bone china teacups, but, as she's just informed her Instagram followers, mugs feel lazy.

Time for Twitter. The only reason she has an account is because Amanda at the book club said it's where the clever people *hang*. She isn't convinced but at least it's less common than that dreadful Facebook run by a schoolboy who looks simultaneously startled and smug.

Joanna's follows @womensart1 (again Amanda's recommendation because it's so important to support women, especially those wonderful poor third world artists who display such naïve colour and imagination).

A photograph appears of a woman cradling her sleeping babe, flanked by her two daughters. It rings every bell in Joanna's head. Perfection. And timely.

'DD!' She calls her assistant, Darling David, to check it out because reading and retweeting on her Twitter feed is the length, depth, and all-I-can-be-bothered scope of her internet skills. 'Darling, get me this photographer on the line. I might have work for him. And print it out for me, there's a love.'

Ten minutes later, DD returns with answers.

'The photographer was Dorothea Lange. She died fifty years ago. The woman was a pea-picker in the dustbowl.'

'Dustbowl?'

'Think *Grapes of Wrath*, Joanna.'

Joanna studies the girls, their faces obscured by what? Shyness? Shame? Whatever. Their hair, though. Despite the black and white print, their hair looks deep blonde with golden streaks. Poverty cuts. Stunning. Shaped and snug to their necks. The girl's hair on the right is special, with a touch of curling abandon to ease the severity. Poverty chic. So *du jour* for these austerity times.

The next day, Joanna hands the high-resolution print-out to Georgio.

'DD says it's a woman from the 1930s Depression, in California or wherever. A pea-picker. I can't believe this isn't staged because if they're so badly off, how is it those little girls have such fabulous haircuts? Whatever. This, Georgio, this is the cut I want.'

Forget the Dead
Sean Lusk

They have gone, after all. And their advice was never right. They slurped their tea and liked to sleep with the windows wide open, even in January. They started crosswords but could never finish them without your help. Also, they began sentences without finishing them but would get cross if you tried to guess what they wanted to say.

They loved you but not well enough to stay alive. And didn't they often tell you they wanted to die? When you were walking along the cliff top and told them that you were thinking of leaving. That time. But then you stayed. And after a while, they seemed themselves again, slurping their tea, opening the windows too wide, laughing at nothing, and sometimes at something.

Forget the dead, for there is no point in having a conversation with them. They never listened anyway, even though they could repeat every word you said to them. Forget their clothes, which seem now to be in every drawer, on every hanger, long after you have taken every last thing to the Oxfam shop. Forget their smell, which was theirs alone and which they really ought to have taken with them, not left here to stop you finishing your sentences, leaving crosswords half-done and making you throw the windows wide open, even in January.

Peak

Colin Lubner

There were four of them on the lift. She was a teacher, AP Physics, twenty-six, a chaperone. Beside her sat two students too young for her to know. At the opposite end reclined an impossibly old man, kicking his skis.

After the chair cleared the final wooded rise and kept rising, she called the base of the mountain for help. She was amazed and grateful for service; that aid was on the way. The two students she didn't know were giggling and taking selfies. The old man's eyes had closed; his chest slowly rose and fell.

Those in the Lodge (and suddenly the Lodge had become capitalized, an entity more than what it now was, too vast and lofty to fully comprehend) had told her not to worry, but she worried, watching the old man. Before closing his eyes, he had removed his helmet, reached down and unclipped his skis. His breaths made little noise. When his skis and helmet had fallen, they had made no sound. He seemed at peace, to know something she did not yet know.

Between them, one of the girls held out her phone and told her to smile. She could see a woman she recognized as herself on the screen. The old man was dead. She was certain, suddenly. Smile, the girl said.

Tomorrow
Jaz Hurford

We used to sit outside on the patio every night. Watch the stars and learn what lips were crafted for. I wasn't in love, that much was certain, but had developed a strange fondness for freckles on tanned arms. Creases mocking blue eyes. I'd heard that the strongest attachments were formed from the most unlikely places, and this terrified me. We fell asleep before it got too cold. Sparks flooded my skin before I could chase them away.

Fresh sunlight gently prodded me awake every morning; glimmers of a new day protruded from the horizon. The sky sat daintily, filled with pretty pastel watercolors. Like a cat, I would half-stretch with raw, unadulterated bliss. That second before consciousness brings thoughts and thoughts bring him. His empty seat looked at me haughtily, daring tears to fall from my eyes again. It sat and watched me this way nearly every morning. Branded me a fool every night. I could never bring myself to look directly into the belly of the beast, as I knew I'd be reprimanded with scornful sigh. *I'm fine, okay?* It stared through me, straight through me, as I willed myself to accept this lie.

And sometimes, it was different. Nights filled with nothing but frenzied longing, muted pain. 'She's out tonight, isn't she?' I'd whisper. He'd say nothing. Merely press his lips to mine. 'Yes, out tonight' he'd mutter almost inaudibly, hands moving in frantic haste.

'She'll be back tomorrow, though. Means you can't stay the night. You'll need to be gone in a couple of hours, if that's alright.'

On nights like these, we didn't watch the stars. I didn't have to chase the sparks away. It got too cold too quickly. Lips trembled, and I simply drove off, quietly. Lines blurred; eyes swam. Streetlights bled into stars.

Good Old-Fashioned British Satanism
Barclay Rafferty

Rain clouds bust around the lighthouse. Its white stone wall boasts black spidery cracks, and through them comes laughter most evenings. If you've ever seen wintry fog across the flatlands, you'll understand the need for land lighthouses. Not many left, mind. Uneconomical, they say – more effective navigational tools available these days. Folk aren't needed at this one, either, truth be told, but we keep an eye on it as a favour. Robots aren't as reliable as they make out.

'We're doing a public good, y'know, Rog.'

Ian hasn't recovered – not fully. Eighteen months ago, he stood in front of a remote foghorn, about fifty metres from the lighthouse, which sounded off unexpectedly as he crossed its path. The blast, he said, could peel paint in a haunted house. And then, well, he shat himself – went mutton for three weeks into the bargain. *Louder than Led Zeppelin*, he reckoned.

'His head's a shed!' Mags, his fancy-woman, called it the steepest fall from grace she's seen, in terms of confidence. 'This is a bloke who was voted Funniest at the Grammar – by the lad who won Funniest at the Grammar.'

'Moral victory, innit,' Ian says.

The village is nucleated. All roads lead to the green. Like a bucolic Scalextric. And at our age, any cobblestone street could be Sniper's Alley. We ankle by the lighthouse, neck a few tins. Fog's thicker than white pepper; slashes of silver cut through it, sounds like back-masking, tongues. 'Communication via carrier bats,' Ian claims. 'Clever bastards, them gofficks. Black mass tonight, then. Like a Dartmoor power-cut out there.'

You hear of old sea-dogs going doolalee in lighthouses. It's the isolation, that or the mercury poisoning. Not a drop for miles here, though, except this drizzle. And we've got each other to ward off Old Beelze'.

Can't see springtime through this fog. We're too old, drunk, happy. *What's the name of that song?* Two shed-heads, jangling with false widows and red-rusted screwdrivers. *What's the name of that song*

– or all those songs? We didgeridoo empty cans, wobble-board ring-pulls, *ah-ooh* to distant rockets...

And what else is there to do, between the blinks that crack the fog?

Swinging Out High
Katie Piper

We swung on the swings, you dislocating yours then jolting back-wards like a slung-out joint, seat rocking like a skateboard, chains slackening and clackening and pinching your fingers, grinding their rust, you, always a little higher, you, with longer legs, a longer dare, a much longer edge.

Everything was an edge with you. I kept up. Just. We swung out together, hair blowing across our faces, my chaste strands slipping through, your peroxide ones stuck in your red lipstick turning them orange, and when you slid them out in vanities way, they stroked tiny slashes across your face.

Then I said, 'Faye, I like your lipstick', and you said, 'It's called Tokyo Nights, don't 'spose you've heard of it? Course you 'aven't.' My sweet confinements grated like a meniscus tear.

All that time we sang 'Sweet Child o' Mine', louder, you louder than me – at the top – when our backs arched like moon-crescents.

The boys were in the burnt-out bandstand, pretending not to no-tice us. They had amyl. It stank like dirty socks to me, and I was still scared of my mum – so I pretended to inhale.

Then Ben rustled over, chin on his scrawny chest, hair lassoing in the wind, hands shoved deep into pockets.

'Amyl?' he said.

He asked me first, not you, and for the first time, I got high.

Out to Lunch
Stella Klein

My father is giving the soup his full attention, tearing off pieces of soft white bread from the basket and stuffing them sideways into his mouth. Leaning back, he belches softly and begins to work a toothpick around his sharp, little teeth.

'Not plumping up much, are you?' he says.

I push my plate away and close my eyes, a wrong moment to picture my science teacher Mr Spritz: the slouch of his jeans and his handsome jaw, the sweeping gestures of his firm, square hands.

'So how is the old bitch?' my father asks.

I tell him my mother is fine. That she is in the Asturias Mountains with a crystal healer named Miguel la Galaxia. That a new lodger from Bratislava has parked a cello in the hall and is filling the fridge with noodles.

My father sighs and orders a slice of strawberry cheesecake, advising the waitress not to lean over quite so much as it could do a man some damage.

'Sabrina makes a great cheesecake,' he says, raising a forkful to his lips.

Devoted, curvaceous Sabrina, expert on the domestic front. Who shares his taste in cheesy jokes and operetta. My father knows nothing of my own talents, of course. That I can flip a perfect omelette and spell words like rhythm and Presbyterian; that when I am stoned, I can read people's minds.

But already he is waving for the bill and I am standing and half-turned towards the door. Already I am with Mr Spritz drinking vodka martinis and blowing smoke rings at the ceiling as he tells me about the lives of protons and protozoa, about the curve of my neck and my curious mind. How he thinks I'll go far. How he likes me just fine.

Attempting Grace
Tara Jackson

I walked into the apartment to find my roommate sobbing on the living room floor: despite my promise that those glue traps never worked, we had caught it, and she'd nearly stepped on the thing as she made her quesadilla, now forsaken in her attempt to promote humane methods of removal: 'I'd deal with it myself,' she whimpered, 'but...' while ethically convicted she was emotionally incapacitated, in no condition to rescue our captive, and as she rambled on about WikiHow's advice to cover the mouse's head and lubricate its tiny feet, I stopped her, saying 'I'll take care of it,' and marched toward the kitchen like I was leaving Gethsemane for Golgotha, praying *God, take this cup*, but of course He didn't, and out of compassion not for the trembling creature in my kitchen but the one in my living room, I found myself crouching on the dusty back stairs, gazing at the skinny legs that, despite being doused in olive oil and stretched to obscene lengths, remained glued to the trap, and I began eyeing the bricks in the stairwell corner until I realized this was a test, I was being tested, and I sighed because I knew what Jesus would do, and he would do it a helluva lot better, so I rebuked the brick, and after excruciating minutes pleading with the mouse, the wretch, by some miracle, finally broke free, and I trudged up the stairs in sweet victory, proclaiming, 'It is finished,' though of course it wasn't, because the next day the damned thing was back, and I felt no guilt as I picked up the brick.

Comfort in Grammar
Marissa Hoffmann

People say it's impossible not to cry when it's your own mother's funeral, but I managed it. People said I was strong. People said my knees didn't buckle, that I didn't seem to need someone to cling to. I checked, and there's no form for daughters in mourning.

I sat at the front. I rolled the service programme, turned it, levelled the crisp edges, turned it more, until that damp neat cylinder kept a perfect shape, even in the waste bin in the ladies' bathroom.

While mourners placed their plates of uneaten sandwich triangles on side-tables, I escaped to a bathroom cubicle. I hung my bag on the door, sat down and thumbed my dictionary. I carried it always: encyclopaedic, illustrated, maroon leather-bound, my treasure house of words.

There: page 562, dog-eared, easy to find – the word 'mother', right-hand column, after 'moth'. If people only took the time to check, they'd know, they'd understand. The mourners were her friends, her colleagues. She was colourful, that's what they said. And if they ever thought of me, colourless, they never said. People knew what she was like, but people are strange; they find moths difficult to love, a nuisance even, but who doesn't love a butterfly? And when the mourners read her headstone – polished granite, with a thirty-year stonework guarantee – they'll read the word 'mother', and they'll think of mothering, they'll think of a kindness and caring.

A dictionary sets it all out, if people would only look. It shouldn't need explaining. I checked. I checked a thousand times, and Mother must have checked too; Mother is a noun. She was only a noun. There's comfort in grammar. Mother was a woman who had borne a child, and that's the black and the white of it.

I ordered the headstone online; it was a limited special offer with a free eighty-word inscription, it really was. So, I went through my dictionary for words for an epitaph, but none fit more perfectly than simply, 'mother'. It has an accuracy that outlives that guarantee. I didn't need eighty words, but customer services could only say, sorry for your loss.

Pessimist
Robert Mason

The new priest is missing four fingers. Whatever accident or surgery caused this, the mutilation is miraculously symmetrical since fore-finger and little finger are absent from both hands.

Knuckles shine, pale and bereft, under his skin as he proffers the Body of Christ. Initially, this was off-putting but, quite soon, distaste was replaced by an appreciation of how efficiently the remaining digits function.

On occasion, their spindly precision brings to mind the perfectly articulated legs of some spider or mantis. At other times, the fingers-and-thumb *pas de trois* is a pleasant reminder of those robot mechanisms, frequently glimpsed in TV programmes about unem-ployment, that have transformed car-making into ballet. The economy and exactitude of movement seem perfect for the job, and, by their very absence, the missing fingers provoke notions of suffer-ing that are fully appropriate.

People are talking, excitedly but quietly, over soft drinks in the parish hall. Their friends, hardly seen at Mass for years, have turned up in modest droves.

But, I fear that when the new priest retires – he is actually a very old priest – a new, new priest will arrive, almost certainly bearing the full complement of fingers. This will be a problem. The way they saveloy around the chalice will be too sensual. The Host will feel greasy on the tongue: pawed, besmirched. Unwelcome, chip-shop associations will intrude.

The congregation will dwindle, I am sure of it.

Flare Stack Skies
Amy Lord

Stacks flare, orange skies phosphorescent with artificial light. She puts the camera to her eye. Click.

A car rushes past, twin beams of light carving a path through the night. On the photograph, the light will blur, the black gloss body of the machine forever in motion. A fleeting moment preserved in time.

She thinks the driver's face was turned towards her. What did he see when he looked at her? A lone woman with a camera clutched in her hands, wandering through a silent industrial estate at night. Was she a mystery to be deciphered? A lost girl.

The driver will become a ghost in print, half a life she'll never know. But she'll always wonder.

A siren cries out. Falls silent just as fast.

He'll be in a car somewhere. She pictures him gazing out the window as the cities flash by, the motorway bearing him south, back to his real life.

Three years and she's not sure he ever meant it.

You're not staying here forever, are you? Don't you want something better?

He never understood. That life could be more than a job in the city and Christmas abroad at his parents' villa. He was all rugby and public school hair. Confidence he'd never had to earn. But not smart enough for Oxbridge; Daddy's money couldn't fix that.

Her obsession with the smokestacks and steelworks, the cooling towers and chemical plants was a cool girl quirk that he indulged, praised and ridiculed in turn.

But for her, it was home. Bleak and beautiful, in the blood.

He was on a northern safari. She was never his forever. It was doomed to end. So she wandered the empty streets at night, more alive behind her lens than he'd ever made her feel.

The Fall of the Bibleman
Jo Gatford

We are twelve in the chapel, and the air is full of stone dust and stifled silence. The chairs beneath us have been worn smooth by bored, shuffling children long dead now but just as scared as we are, staring up at pretty glass pictures of death and sunshine that look back down upon us with disapproval.

Some poor sucker is wearing a bible mascot costume so ridiculously square he can barely make it down the aisle as he hands out red pocket bibles with sharp-edged plastic covers, hastily clipped off some production line and stamped with gold letters. *Free religion! Get 'em while they're impressionable!* Some earnest young thing trying to save us even though we're too young to sin properly; even though it's already too late. As if we need more promises of salvation. We are old enough to know there is no three-act structure and no saving the day and no consequences for people who get to decide the definition of a sin. Ah, those sanctioned sins. Those day-to-day sins. The ones we don't talk about. Because who would believe us anyway?

I can't remember if it's you or me who is sitting on the aisle; which one of us shifts our outward foot just so, to make the bibleman trip. Either way, he thinks it's me, and he looks up from the herringbone floor and into my face with a disgust I've never seen since on a human being; with such force it makes me grip my bible so hard the corner bites into the flesh between my thumb and forefinger.

You call it a stigmata, later, in an underbreath whisper as we stand in the headmaster's office and pretend to be sorry, and the moment the words are alive there is no stopping the flood and we break, folding, holding onto one another's elbows, hawking like donkeys. The bibleman is there, too, out of his cubic costume, with an expression of pity on his tight little face now – as if he is sorry for our very souls for still being able to laugh – as if we think this breathless rebellion makes us free.

The Squirrel
Richard Levitt

After she accepted my offer of a lift, I worried about my car.

The 'Enormo-Porsche' was a mistake. Five years ago, when I collected it gleaming and white from the dealership, I wondered if I could change my mind. Now I've retired, it embarrasses me more. Still, my children love the plush seats sculpted into the rear.

On the threshold of the car park, she turns and waves to the others.

Perhaps, when I added my name to the lift-share board, my judgement was clouded by nine days of noble silence.

I was lucky to be allocated a single room. It's hard to imagine sharing without talking, decoding your roommate through observation, except you weren't supposed to observe or distract.

I had one conversation during the nine days. I asked a facilitator if I too could meditate in a chair. My knees were killing me. He encouraged me to work through my pain.

Each meditation was interrupted by the piped voice of our guru, who had died years before. Resurrected by tech, he instructed, exhorted and encouraged. At some point, he described an impoverished woman, inconsolable at the loss of her few possessions. Anyone might suffer from attachment.

When noble silence ended, and we could exchange details, I was itching to share my misgivings. To my surprise, my companions had none.

She too is convinced. She's been living at the retreat for three months, working unpaid as a cook. She has long flowing curls. She smiled at me when we were introduced, a warm open smile between initiates. I decided to play along.

The squirrel hesitates. We've been discussing veganism, the kitchen's use of extra virgin olive oil, the merits of paying what you think the experience is worth, the ubiquitous nature of karma.

The two-tonne car is elevated at least an inch, front first, then rear. I see the squirrel briefly in the mirror, a bundle of fur on a curved strip of tarmac framed by oak trees, golden green in the autumn sunlight.

Trimmed

Johanna Robinson

'I need scissors. Will you help?' I lift my hair, stringy and limp. Already a disguise, but not enough. The nurse nods and points to a room off the stairwell before she hurries off. The room's empty, but there's a small window, veined with cracks, where the soot has settled. There are bars on the outside, and I lean my arms on the windowsill. My knuckles, my wrists, look like the pebble skeletons I used to lay out in the woods.

Below, on the street, there are so many layers of living going on, it seems possible that I could slide in between them. The nurse appears, a pair of scissors tucked up her sleeve. She closes the door, and I think *she trusts me*, and she must think the same.

'Sit down.' She kneels and pulls my hair back. There's a tug as she begins to cut. The scissors are blunt and chew slowly through my hair. She breathes on the back of my neck, in time with the closing of the blades. She makes a noise, as though she's trying to solve a puzzle, and starts to thin my hair out into sections, laying them over my shoulders like tapering roots. Each snip sounds like it could be the last.

'I didn't think you'd get out of here alive,' she says, as she drops pieces of me onto the wooden floor. 'You're a tough one.'

There's such a gap between my shoulders and my ears now, a gap grows between who I was and who I might be. When her fingers catch my temple, she thinks she's hurt me, but it's the memory of Mam washing my hair that she has scratched. She cuts until there's nothing left for the wind to dance with.

She ties a knot in my shirt at my side and wraps the bandage tight around my chest. She winds, pats, leaning into me and back out, and when she runs out of length, she secures the end.

'Thank you,' I say to her back as she leaves, and I wonder when I will get used to the tightness around my chest.

She Will Dance
Lydia Clark

She was a child that took first and thought later. The scar that gloved her left hand told that story. Her mother never boiled rice again.

In the audition room, the oddness of it stood out amongst the rows of girls, and she had been secretly thankful. She could out-chaîné anyone, of course, but she enjoyed how watchable it made her. The upright men and women behind the table – dusted off dancers from long ago seasons – spotted her imperfection as soon as they glided in. They smiled at her triple pirouette in a way that proved she had more than made up for it.

There was no thought needed. *Elle dansera*, her old Parisian ballet teacher said, and she filled the application forms herself. She would be accepted into the best school. *Elle dansera, elle sera sur scène.* Her tired mother picked her up at night. Her boy was left at home, sleeping with the lights on. Her girl, planning a future, leagues away.

She took the letter from the doormat before her mother got home from her weekend job. Perhaps she would be angry she hadn't waited, but it had been weeks, and the Times New Romaned name in its rustling window belonged only to her. Cleaning caravans was her mother's only ambition, and here she was, on the cusp of winning her own.

Her mother came home with the collar of her polo upturned and knew. The white envelope appeared to glow against her daughter's angry skin; almost as striking, almost as wrinkled. It wasn't the past; it wasn't the remnants of that dreadful moment telling the story now. Here she was – her dancing girl, who took what she wanted at whatever cost – finally thinking. For there was nothing to take this time.

Geology
Ali Bacon

Years later, he got in touch to say he would be passing through and would she like to meet for a catch-up? 'Catch-up' probably wasn't the word he used, but she took its meaning, *nothing heavy*.

She had wangled an hour off and went to meet him in the foyer; all above board, complete with introductions, *my old friend, my ex-colleague, my ex...*

They couldn't stay here, so she drove him away from the city, a gem in a soft green bowl, through the straggling village that wound up the hill.

They mulled over things that had happened, to people they knew, to jobs and families.

The city had fallen away. The gradient on the last ascent surprised her, and she fumbled the gears, 'I come this way every day, believe it or not.'

She pulled up on a narrow verge on the highest corner, where for a glorious instant, the road confronted this other view before dipping away round the bend.

She had always meant to stop here but, hurrying from work to home and back again, she never had. This was the world in between, and she had been saving it for him, for the set of his shoulders, the small frown of concentration she'd forgotten until this afternoon.

They got out and looked over the escarpment, a vertiginous swoop from crest to valley floor, puzzling over the surprise of it, debating the geology.

Time might have stopped, but he had to get back, and they soon ran out of words.

It was only a view, a hollow in the land speckled by a small flock of sheep, bordered by two stone houses back-to-back: a place of safety where the earth's crust had once heaved and rucked, leaving something like the wrinkle in a sheet.

Painters and Potters at Play
Leonard Kress

Several men check their iPhones for scores – Ohio State Buckeyes and whoever – so they fail to notice the girl who's less than half their age as she lowers herself to the couch and falls asleep. Her arm dangles, and her fingers splay over the edge and graze the carpet. If the dog chained outside the door were let in, he'd surely rush to lick them. And she, in her wine-stupor, might let a tiny smile twitch across her face.

No one can explain her presence. She arrives at the party amid the first rush and quickly makes the rounds of those other men – the artists – who aren't even aware there is a Buckeyes game. She drapes her bare, inked arm over their hunched shoulders as she screws her face in closer and closer and locks in their gaze like a relentless prosecutor whose cross-examination won't even allow a wife or girl-friend's defense.

But it's too late for the artists. They're already occupied with clay glaze compatibilities and the brand-new extruder that the hostess is showing off. This girl wants something from them – free studio space, exhibitions, art supplies, but the men she slots are playing the broke and bitter game, their best canvasses held hostage by fantastic gallery swindles. Their best work relegated to moldy storerooms collectors will never enter.

One by one, the artists break free, choosing wine, sirloin tips, brie, and puff pastries, followed by more wine – over this muse. Yet she is still here. They can't see that she is inside them and has been for decades. Though now, when they bother to look, they only see her chest heaving in slumber, her dark hair spilling onto the carpet in rivulets. Her body limp enough to transport to the guest room – while everyone else is engrossed in oldies and unsettled scores – a place that's been readied for them with turps, brushes, and stretched gessoed canvas.

March
Alan Beard

At the hairdressers, the woman with her gloved fingers in my hair goes on about a party she went to last night. Works do, her husband kept dancing with other men's wives. Dignitaries too, one of them one of them psycho things who do profiles is it of the workforce, offices. Something. He went to Buckingham Palace. I mean, they live in a different world. Not something we'll ever do, is it?

Not something I'll do anyway, I say, laid back looking up at her. Right, right. She's puzzled by this different place that exists, her husband disappearing into it, bit by bit. He's been promoted. Grown a moustache, got some new shoes on his own. Turn ups to show them off.

All the staff wear purple-ish tracksuits. Radio One is blaring away, retro disco, which reminds her – there was a band, a whatdoyoucallem, brass band. I said can't you put some oomph into it, you know, some jazz? And they played Jungle Book. Her husband lapped it up, apparently, shaking his head like a madman. As if he had a trunk or something. Stomping about. Everybody around, his adoring colleagues, laughing.

I lay back with her melancholy hanging face above me, clogged pores visible, my dyeing hair stroked, imagining her husband inserting his cock anywhere it will go.

Vintage
Joyce Ann Wheatley

Catherine collects buttons in a pink oval tin. On the lid, ladies in high-necked blouses with ruffled cuffs and collars carry fluted green umbrellas like turtle shells to shade them from the sun. When she shakes it, buttons clatter, rattle and echo. Her mother says, 'I can't hear myself think' and snatches them away. Catherine throws a tantrum and, when she yanks her buttons back, they spill across the floor. Little secrets bounce, roll and skitter behind drapes, under chairs and tables and down the hall. Her mother slams the door. A babysitter helps gather up the buttons but keeps some sparkly ones for herself.

In high school, Catherine rummages TJ Max, eBay and Craigslist. She's a Teenage Fashionista. She haunts flea markets, Trader K's and Salvation Army. She masks their musty smells with an embroidered ecru handkerchief and lilac scent. She snips off vintage buttons, posts pictures of her favorites, and she's a Pinterest sensation. Her mother says, 'Enough!' so Catherine sells a few on Etsy. When teachers say Catherine has a good eye and head for business, her mother says, 'Nonsense.' Catherine zips her lips and twirls the toggles on her coat.

Mother helps out in Catherine's Button Emporium & Museum's Gift Shoppe. She dusts and straightens and hums 'She's Come Undone,' a sad song by Ultimate Spinach. In counselling, Catherine confesses Mother is a burden. Catherine lectures on 'The Progress of Fasteners: Zippers, Buttons, Snaps and Hooks' and disparages Velcro, which 'lacks imagination.' Lovers come and go. They poke tongues through her earlobes, pin petalled discs to her nipples. One shows a fierce attachment – pearly bauble in her bellybutton, stitches little blue anchors below her clavicle and says, 'Sail away with me,' but she dreads their future popping. Alone, Catherine's fingers thread through bins of buttons, dribbles them palm to palm. She's lulled by all their histories, like seashells rustling in a pail, or piles of old, sun-bleached bones.

The Marriage of the Sea
Sharon Telfer

They step on starburst, herringbone, chequerboard; each room, a different honeyed parquet floor. Glass chandeliers drop pulled-candy tentacles. The modern art baffles them, splodging the palazzo walls like the damp in their first, long-ago subterranean flat. But there's aircon and drawn blinds. When they emerge, blinking, into the light, the heat slaps.

The fish market slips with melting ice. The air smells liquid and salt. The stallholder slices them shrimp, a baby's thumb so fresh they eat it raw. Crabs wag wearied, pinioned claws. Fish glisten – silver, coral, blue – eyes at the very point of dimming.

Every year, for a thousand years, they read, the city has married the sea: rowers bend, fanfares blare, flags whip, a wedding band is cast like an anchor into the lagoon.

We wed thee, sea, as a sign of true and everlasting domination.

They lean on bridges, push tightening rings round hot, swollen fingers. They've billed it a second honeymoon. Both know it's a last chance.

They flee the crowds down passages that tang of piss and shit.

'That film, the little girl who drowned!'

They lose themselves in dead-end alleys, beneath listless washing.

'The red coat, the terrible killer!'

They find a green courtyard away from the furious sun. Only when they've finished their picnic, do they see the warnings for rat poison.

Their skin pinks and peels. They churn up and down the Grand Canal, the vaporetto gears grinding like a waking monster.

'Everything in this city is stolen.'

'Even the city is stolen from the sea.'

The promenade glitters sharp as knives. Tourists rustle, phones go up. The tug hauls in the giant liner, more spacecraft than cruise ship, its alien decks taller than the terracotta tiles and the bronze horses, stranger than the shining angels, than the winged lion itself.

They clasp masks to their faces and drink bittersweet Aperol Spritz. At midnight, with each strike of the great bell, the ground ripples under their feet.

They come apart in separate dreams. A chandelier blows out groping suckers. Thick water swallows a golden ring. The sea shakes off its domination and rises to reclaim its own.

It Does Not Matter How You Go,
As Long As You Go to Seoul
CS Bowerman

Snow on the winter beach echoes the white horses on the squally waves yonder. Another two wooden fishing boats have been washed ashore like a pair of lost oriental slippers. Pallid wooden bows hide their cargo, not of sandfish and squid, but chalky skeletons starved and frozen while fishing on the East Sea. They are 600 miles from home, grounded finally on this Japanese beach of relentless wind turbines and dirt seeped sand.

To return home was perhaps too difficult. They have old engines and no GPS. Ragged chalky sails unable to hold tightly to hoary seasonal winds. To return home was perhaps too shaming. Not enough fish in their blanched string nets. Targets too high to achieve in these pale vessels. Or maybe to return home bereft was not their purpose. Proverbs fed into their eager hearts taught them that at the end of hardship comes happiness and that it is possible to pluck a star from the sky – or perhaps the king crab from the empty deep. There is an order to a successful life: you must sleep before you can dream.

The fisherman's catch has become worth dying for, worth burial without funeral, an unclaimed grey cremation. A new madness to take small pearly boats too far out to sea. Each failed attempt a struggle for honour, each smooth wreck a testament to irrepressible hope. The ivory turbines continue to turn, fair wind or ill, snow or gales. Determined they will make something from nothing. The ancestors would be proud.

In Bed With Melon Bread
Leonie Rowland

When we were standing in the convenience store looking intently at bread, you asked me what I was thinking, and I said: melon bread has a better bedside manner than any man I've been with. You must have mistaken this for encouragement because you reached for a chocolate twist with confidence in your eyes, but really it was just the truth.

I visited your flat a week later, and the twist was displayed on your kitchen shelf like a motivational quote. I thought at first that you had bought another one, but you glanced at it repeatedly as you made my coffee, and when you left the room, I checked the sell-by date. It seemed to me that you were keeping souvenirs of something that hadn't happened. I could feel it watching us with little chocolate eyes.

You started sending me slices of toast after that. They arrived in paper packages. The first time I opened one, crumbs spilt all over the floor. *Attentive*, I said to myself as I fetched the hoover and took a bite.

You almost had me then; I liked the time you had taken to toast the bread. I'm nervous that toasters will become obsolete when life gets too busy, you see, and it was soothing to know that you still used one.

The caveat was this: that night, after deciding we should be together, I climbed into bed with my daily melon bread, and I was struck by the quiet. I lit a candle and took a bite. Then, I imagined you asking for a taste.

You should have bought your own, I said as if you were there. I was glad, as the melon-flavoured cream sweetened the taste that had settled in my mouth, that you were not.

She was a drift of wood in the rainbelt. She knew the touch of sand-eased granite, the wash of fired icemelt. The fog draped heavy on her porous pine bones.

She was a work of the Pacific. It had made her as it had made the High Cascades.

Soon, she had a reason for leaving. In her exile, she knew sun-molt, dead skies, fractured dirt in lands of tin and soot. Water was precious, and she could not weep.

In those days, she dreamed of a bay, a bubble of the Sound. A brow of firs shaded its beach; it glowed with drifting spars. In the morning haze were things she could not see. They were stickle-backed and dangling from their skyhooks, nails down.

A shape of pebbles was familiar at her feet. It rose and walked in outline. Drifting ash papered its face and sinews. It spoke, but she could not hear. It stretched out sudden arms like firebrands, its flame-tipped fingers reaching for her mouth. She did not answer. The fire burst up its face and hair, fanned down its legs and feet. Its burning was of dread, and she backed fast along the beach. Doggedly, it followed, packing blazing hands in fists. It badly needed water, but it sought out only hers.

And that was how she knew it had a name: *Father*.

The talons of the ones who watched emerged. Their fatal swoops sheared pebble from pebble, ash from dust. Their rapture opened her wells and freed her ears. Content, the flock flew hazewards, empty.

The fire sang in embers. The ash laughed into mist. The Sound rolled gently up the beach, and there was smoke. The shape, and its man, were past.

Alone, she lay between the water and the land, and slept.

Stacie
Linda McMullen

After a prolonged courtship, with occasional outings in a racy Corvette, the couple in Emily's Barbie house finally enjoyed a brisk wedding and a picnic – like Greg and I once did. Although Emily's never heard that particular family story. I kiss her forehead, congratulate Barbie and Ken on achieving plastic nirvana, and announce human/plaything bedtime. Emily hunches toward her pajama drawer... then slips past me, giggling riotously, pirouetting past the bathroom and the closet, holding the triumphant doll-couple aloft.

Greg, from the living room, 'I thought you were putting her to bed?'

At our last appointment, the therapist instructed him to use 'I'-language.

'Halfway there,' I call back, fortuitously seizing the wriggling first-grader about the waist before she launches herself downstairs. We complete the purgatorial bedtime checklist in fifty-seven minutes flat. My body slopes into my heart-shaped divot in the couch.

'Did you change the sheets?' asks Greg. 'She didn't make it last night. Again.'

I had said last week that she'd outgrown it. And *I* made the same assertion yesterday.

'I thought you did, this morning.'

'I *also* had an early call. And when I got home, I did the dishes. I took out the trash and the recycling. And I'm doing the taxes,' replies Greg. A peacock-tail document fan adorns our coffee table. He's a forensic accountant. At Deloitte. And not at Deloitte.

'Emily wanted you to take a break and watch her,' I say. 'You missed some season finale-level stuff. Barbie and Ken finally ended their Pam-and-Jimming—'

'She can't sleep in piss-covered sheets,' says Greg. And he waits.

I recall the therapist rhapsodizing about love-languages, and manage to escape the divot's disproportionate gravitational field. I extract a delighted Emily from her bed and spend another thirty-nine minutes returning her to it.

When I come back downstairs, circa 10:23 p.m., Greg passes me the completed tax forms. 'Do you want to take a look?'

Balances tap-dance before my eyes. 'Did you deduct the daycare?'

'It's not worth it.'

I breathe, breathe, breathe. The therapist said to do that, too.

'Mommy?' calls Emily, from her bedroom. 'Can I get a Stacie doll? Barbie and Ken need a kid.'

You Were Never Good with Needles
Charles Prelle

She mechanically daubs you with antiseptic. A piece of cotton wool. You make nervous small talk. Arbitrary clicks and beeps to fill the silence. Your muscles tense as it pierces your skin. You feel exposed. Inside out. She applies a plaster which falls off in the shower. You watch as it circles the drain, massaging the purple bruise with hot water until you go numb.

You're in a sterile office. Hand sanitiser and paper sheets. A fluorescent bulb twinkles overhead. Moments obscured. He's speaking, but you've stopped listening. The electric whirr of a machine fills your ears. Lives being sucked out. Transplanted. Your body deconstructs. You're a test tube. A guinea pig. A pincushion.

You return home to your wife and daughter. You watch her play with her dollhouse. She brushes the wiry curls so gently it makes you weep. A pot simmers in the kitchen, releasing perfumes of garlic and basil. Your wife kisses you a greeting. She asks about your day. You say it was fine.

You lie beside her, watching the rise and fall of her breast. You draw the sheets around her bare shoulders. Impotent armour. You shake two white pills from a brown plastic bottle. They roll around in your palm like dice.

You're wearing a green hospital gown. Plastic tubing coils around you. Equipment hisses angrily. The poison enters your bloodstream. Drip by drip. Later you shed parts of yourself like orange leaves.

She cradles your tiny hand in hers. Dried tears set sticky on your cheeks. You imagine the needle penetrating, massaging the spot where it entered in tiny loops with your thumb. With a soothing whisper, she closes your eyes. Mummy's here. She gently kisses your wound as you drift further from consciousness, the warmth of her lips lingering long after you wake.

Date Night
Steven Moss

We feel old so take the train East for Knickerbocker glories in a retro bar, to look for the tingle of cream on our souls.

Taking our seats, wafting our faces with plastic menus, we spend hours choosing desserts with fancy names. Here, everything feels like hope: the cheerleader figurines, the varsity jackets framed with a backdrop of Doo-Wop, even the bar got a sweet timbre finish.

The tender sees our order, nods and smiles, points a finger, says 'These are for you,' and clicks and grins, fires down two tall shakes, pink and yellow meringue with white ice cream swimming in glass, topped with ruby crystals and we reach out our hands and we gasp.

We kiss, consider the train journey back but, instead, stay out to go looking for a nearby hotel taking last-minute bookings.

It takes some convincing, convincing the receptionist at such a late hour, with the establishment being the type wanting cards and *no cash*, but we sway them, with our sensible coats and good manners.

Still, though, they ask us, 'Is there much to declare?'

We place our cases on the counter. Toughened carbon, personalised; flip the catches and there lay nestled gold in padded foam, two brightly battered hand-stitched teddy bears, priceless, side by side.

Rekindled but wary, we settle their mute reservations; whistle a tune, tap them a rhythm, we guide them gently upright, and in response, they slick down their mohair and step onto the counter to dance.

Now this: Our bear soles spinning, paws touching, matching tattoos pressed together, and Goldilocks dyed into skin.

The Vengeful Woman's Cookbook
Mary Francis

We're scaling down the fight, from red-hot to simmering. A delicate procedure. Any misplaced word or noise can send the heat rocketing up again, filling the kitchen with flames and steam.

This is my domain, and she knows it. I cook the meals. I serve them. She doesn't know where the cheese grater goes. As if she doesn't live in the house; she's just a guest, passing through, paying no rent and tidying away clean dishes into the wrong drawers.

There's always something cooking in my kitchen. She knew that when she married me.

This fight has been stewing for weeks, since her brother and his wife came over for dinner. Dear God, her family is tedious. We've been together long enough there's no point trying to cover my feelings. I've always been forthright, anyway, a dominant flavour. She knew that, too, when she married me.

I'm the chilli and you're the cheese, I told her once. I'm the curry and you're the lassi. We're a fusion of spice and nice, balancing each other out. Without her, I'd be unbearable. Without me, she'd be like her white sliced brother.

She says she wants calm family dinners. Mild flavours and bland conversation. Pulling away from the heat as if she never liked it.

Who would want a meal without a kick to it? Who orders plain, boring food, served up predictably, day after day, meat and two veg on the table at 6 p.m., the suburban nightmare? We need fireworks and fusion, excitement and passion. That's what makes a meal an experience; what makes a relationship stay alive.

I don't hold a grudge. But I cook the food the way I like it, and tonight I add extra chilli. And a dash of lime.

Your Version of Beauty Does Not Define Me
Iona Winter

I used to wear my gumboots to ballet class, reluctantly leaving them at the door to twirl in a horrible pink leotard. After that came Irish dance lessons, where a tiny woman wielded a large wooden ruler to slap our fragile legs.

No words were spoken. Being there was better than at home.

Once you said something about 'fucking it out' of me. I didn't reply because I was too damn shocked. You had no idea what I'd survived.

I need to tell you that seeing the innate beauty in nature is what saved me. I never asked you to.

Nowadays, I listen when women in toilet stalls reel off reams of paper. They've probably flooded and are wadding their undies in shame, like me. And still we check the back of our dark pants religiously, despite light colours being a no go zone and surfboard-sized pads a feature.

Nobody speaks about that either.

When I watch old ladies helping their old men with worn-out bodies, I think they have forgotten, that a crone bathes in the wisdom of darkness, her blood sealed. And oh, how powerful that makes her.

So I call myself a bloody queen and laugh at this new shape of me – the set of lips against teeth wider, arms guarding nothing but themselves, with a heart that remains open.

And I know that inside me resides infinite beauty.

Treasure Island
Sue Pearson

Days of rain have transformed the old woodland reserve. She removes the lead from her spaniel's neck, and he bounces off, following his nose to new and familiar smells in the undergrowth. Disturbed, crows caw hoarsely amongst the trees.

She wades ankle-deep through new streams to dry land. Stops to consider the rippling pools surrounding her. Gold and russet leaves spin, reflecting sunlight into forest shadows. Her memory echoes with the cries and shouts of children hurtling through the undergrowth in pursuit of adventure.

It's easier to wear the leash across her body. Her pockets are so cluttered. In the right, phone, tissues and poo bags. In the left, a bag of dog treats – pieces of cheese to bring him to heel.

She pushes her head, shoulder and arm through the expanded loop of rope. It catches on a fold of her hood. She reaches behind, fumbling, and senses him. The bogeyman of old. That lurking nondescript figure marooned in shadow.

He comes behind her now.

Let me, he breathes.

His calloused palm brushes her frozen knuckles. Long, deft fingers release the edge of material from the tangle. They gently cage her hand, compelling it to caress the twisting red plait of rope, as one with him.

Nice this, he whispers.

Tentatively he settles their hands upon her hair. Probing through loose strands, he strokes the soft flesh behind her ear.

His forehead comes to rest heavily against her skull. Dark hair falls across her face. Tangled. She smells burnt wood and earth. And the lead is held taut against her throat as weathered lips dally by her ear.

I smell treats, he murmurs, sharp teeth grazing her skin.

On you, he groans, breath wet as marshland.

She gropes in her pocket and pulls them free.

Here, she rasps.

Crows rise, cackling, into the sky.

Cheese, just a little piece of cheese.

It's been so long for poor Ben Gunn.

I

Vincent Calder

What do you do when you get home at night? When meek fingers fiddle with keys and aching feet carry you through your door, into your quiet, still flat.

Shall I tell you what I do?

When I've click clicked through my front lock and turned on the lights and closed the door behind me. When I am by myself again. I go into the bedroom, turning out the living room lights.

I stand by my bed, and I look into the mirror. I start with my clothes. I remove my coat, hat, jumper, jacket, boots, shoes, high heels. I unbutton my shirt. I peel my T-shirt over my head, catching my chin. I unclasp my belt, I unzip my skirt. I shed my jeans. I unclip my bra. I unfurl tights. I strip off socks. I step out of boxer shorts. I wriggle off knickers.

Naked then I straighten and stand. I take off my wig, slip off my toupee, pluck out my beard. I unstick my breasts, I unclip my penis, discard my vagina. I rip out my eyebrows, my eyelashes follow. My ears after, then my nose. My mouth goes next, first one lip and then the other.

I need my eyes. I need to see to furl back the duvet and arrange the pillow. Once I am warm again in bed, the lights out. That is when I remove the last. Green eyes, brown eyes, blue eyes, grey, hazel, black. I take them out one after the other and put them back in the box on the bedside table, back where they belong with the others.

What keeps you awake at night? Back in my natural state, wiped clean, stripped bare, I think of nothing. And I sleep.

Tremors at the Edge of an Exploding Bomb
Kay Sandry

You have a secret.

It is heavy.

It lives in untold thoughts, lays dormant in waking dreams, and it resonates in barely registered nuances.

It sounds like the song of choir boys, their inviolate voices lifted aloft to the heavens in adoring purity. It beats to the march of soldiers' boots, tramping and weary. It is in the tear that never falls.

It is hidden so deep that lifetimes pass before it is exposed. It echoes in the cries of a new-born baby, blares in the blast of words said in anger, and whispers in the talk, intimate and heavy, moments after making love before you're claimed by sleep.

It is camouflaged by the scent of roses, smoothed over with Oil of Ulay. It is brushed into shape with an ivory-backed hairbrush. It rests in the folds of silk undergarments, smelling lightly of lavender, neatly folded in mahogany drawers.

It crackles in the brown paper bag of liquorice pomfret cakes.

It rolls in the crumbs of rock buns that you chase around a patterned china plate with the tip of your finger and then pop into your mouth. It burns in the heat of the oven as bread rises and simmers in the water of the kettle.

It tastes like Sunday dinners, and it shocks like oranges being thrown against the wall.

It feels like the softest skin your lips have ever brushed against.

It has the colour of fear and wears the invisible cloak of silence.

It aches like your body being lowered into the ground
and
it rejoices in all those who mourn your passing.

~

You had a secret.

All your life, you stood at the edge of an exploding bomb and the tremors it sent out were absorbed by the strength of your mind and were never betrayed by any weakness of your body.

Now that you have passed, it is we who are left who must deal, unprepared, untrained,

with this explosion that did not come from the sky

but detonated instead
in
the very heart
of
family.

Punctuation
Anne Howkins

Her abandoned paperbacks sulk in accusing piles, spilling their chapters onto bare floorboards. A few words cling defiantly to the well-thumbed pages; the rest relinquish their attachment to the paper.

He slumps on the sofa, ignoring the restless fiction. In the loveless dark inconsolable rivulets of Times New Roman trickle towards him, point by sullen point. They demand attention, yearning to be re-animated by a reader. Sometimes he runs his fingers through the streams, panning for happiness, letting misery drift by. When he closes his fists, the brittle letters shatter. Black dust drifts, covering everything, like a fingerprint dusted crime scene.

Paragraphs decay, breaking into sentences, then phrases, to pool darkly against skirting boards and chair legs. He doesn't notice the full stops, dots and commas rolling around, eventually settling into the indentations her red stilettos left in his newly stripped floor a lifetime of loss ago. The brackets and ampersands form a trail of curls drifting across the floor before they slip through gaps in the boards. As structure vanishes, the words blur into a stream of unconsciousness.

When he drags himself off to his solitary insomnia, silverfish feast on book glue. Blank pages liberated from their spines slide into slippery traps for his bare feet. Woodlice cluster, gorging on the sheets until the pages resemble lace doilies. In the gloom, the floor shimmers.

He ignores the threatening manila accumulating in the hall. There is no heat or light in the house, and the log basket contains nothing but woodlice and mouse droppings.

The cold drives him to burn her books. He rakes through the ash each night, hoping to find the vestiges of *love, forever, happy,* as the skeleton pages disintegrate.

Without the punctuation of her, he can make no sense of the world.

Local Time, Everywhere
Tom O'Brien

The world caught fire early Thursday evening, local time.

The Metro cryptic brittled under my fingertips. What had the paper been in another life; a marriage licence, prescriptions, a death certificate?

Sun through your cut in the blackout sheet lit clues I never solve. I'd held the ladder, took the knife from your hand.

'We can't live only in the dark,' you said when I fretted about heatburn.

The weight of heat pressed one wall on to me, and a rubber stink from outside scalded my nose. The last time they relaid the road, they used concrete mixed with tyres no one wanted to remould. It needled dry tears bad enough to lever me from my chair.

In the front doorway, I shielded my eyes and saw the bubbling black line beyond the dust garden. The abandoned car where we'd crept out to drink moonlight gin had sunk to its wheelrims. All around, cracks of ignition imitated the cackle of birds who once had the freedom of the sky.

The distant low thump of something large and liquid taking flame shook the old clues loose. Everything I'd seen through another door, years ago, shifted like words with shadowed meaning. I could look past you, unasleep; look beyond your slack and ringless fingers to the mirror where the gold band hung alone with its reflection. Your whisper to me that this was no accident.

I fill seven blank squares with an ink-dry pen.

The skin on the arm I'd used to shield my eyes blisters from elbow to wrist. The starlings tattooed there lift in false flight before tumbling to the molten flesh below.

I punch the sky with that weeping arm, roaring to you, but the blazing air is done with hauling our complaints. The world is not like you; she has nowhere else to go. She'll burn us off and start again, and I breathe, 'Yes my sister, yes, I know just how you feel.'

His Best Jumper
R J Bailey

When they first got together, he said he wasn't the romantic type. He tied a loose thread from his best jumper around her wrist instead of holding her hand. He wore it often and joked that if she left, she'd destroy the jumper entirely. She could feel the tug of it even now; the faint pop as the close-knit unravelled stitch by stitch when she lingered by shop windows or stepped out into the street too soon. He would cry out in alarm as the hem of his jumper leapt another inch, and the ragged woollen string grew taut but didn't snap.

Today, for a lark, they were promenading along the pier. The tourists were gone, couldn't stand the rain, but they liked it just fine. Heads together, they strolled with touching shoulders under an umbrella; their own little island of dry air, floating amid the raindrops towards the end of the pier, a bubble in a storm.

She felt the clean salt air on her wrist, rubbed a little raw by the woollen thread, and the roar of the sea could have been her heart beating. She bit her lip at one of his jokes, buffoonish but eager, and tasted rust. He held the umbrella, and her right arm was getting soaked.

She was listening, but in all honesty, her attention was drawn to the unmoving line of the horizon. If she didn't look down, but kept her chin perfectly level, it looked like she was walking on water, stretching out into forever with her little pocket of dry air.

He stopped suddenly to deliver the punchline. The tether tugged at her wrist, but she slowed too late, and another line of knitting burst. She stumbled, drawn back by the feeling of his unravelling. He sulked, his joke cut short, and she turned to him.

It was such a shame, she thought, that the pier was so short. She would have liked to keep walking a little longer, despite the rain. With her dripping right hand, she quietly unplucked the thread from around her wrist. They'd made enough of a mess with his jumper.

Cees and Gees
Lauren Collett

'Stalactites, from the ceiling, with a *cee*,' said our guide, 'And stalagmites, from the ground, with a *gee*.' And with that, she gestured around the cave, as if to say, *over to you, cave.*

The ones from the ceiling I could understand. The cumulative effect of drips and gravity. Made sense, even to me. But the ones coming up out of the ground? Baffling. I wondered if, eventually, the *cees* and *gees* would meet in the middle. Fuse together. Probably there was a scientific reason that this couldn't happen. Probably it was something that I couldn't possibly understand.

'Now I switch off lights,' said the guide, monotonously. 'Some of you have never seen total darkness.'

A grunt of accord behind me. 'Even with your eyes closed,' he said. His fist tightened on my coat. I lurched back.

'Wrong shoes,' he said. He was right, they were; but he'd bought me these shoes – kitten heeled, open, did nothing for me, short as I am – and he'd been sad that I hadn't yet worn them.

'You don't like them,' he'd said that morning.

Well, I didn't want to upset him.

The lights went out, and it was as if they'd never been on. We all surveyed nothingness in our own ways. Drips tip-tapped endlessly to remind us that the *cees* and the *gees* kept on keeping on.

Then he let go.

My shoulders dropped with my coat, and I felt, all at once, cushioned by the damp emptiness, as if I could breathe underwater. I put my hand to my face, and it was so deliciously cold. Was this what it was like, to be touched by me? What a balm, this hand would be, to a feverish infant! What limitless comfort I seemed to possess! That hand vibrated with the same implausible stamina as those bewildering *gees*, built from nothing, coming up from nowhere.

A whimper from somewhere. A child, perhaps, afraid.

The lights came back on. I turned and saw that he was sitting on his haunches. Head down, hands clutching his knees.

I took off my shoes, the rock like home, and I waited.

Space
Jessica Mitchell

They made an offer on a house with too many bedrooms. They joked about fucking in every room. About SPACE. One calling out to the other: 'Where are you?' Silence as thick as cream, and not enough furniture. SPACE, they said. It was always a kind of shout. Think of it!

Inside there were keys for everything and instruction manuals and in the attic a handmade sign that said 'Toy Factory'. That first spring, they planted bulbs for the summer, and when the summer was over, they dug them up again.

It was a family house. Everyone agreed that it was a family house.

The cat never got comfortable. He thought that they were keeping secrets. Howled at each closed door. Scratched. Only to be disappointed when he entered. His dark eyes narrowing as he realised it was merely empty. Another empty room.

She lay on the carpet in the bedroom that they called the third bedroom. And she slept in the bed in the bedroom that they called theirs. The only room in which they had fucked, actually. The fucking always only a means to an end. The mechanics laid bare, like the walls.

The SPACE is great, she said, too brightly, when people asked. We don't know what to do with it.

Failure to Engage
Kali Richmond
SUMMER 2020 FIRST PLACE

She longs to work with animals; not a unique childhood yearning, but she believes her passion is why out of four hundred girls, *she* has been chosen to attend the seminar at the zoo. In truth, it has more to do with lifting up the vulnerable, those who require guidance, and so she is guided into the auditorium in hope of galvanisation, for she bunks off a lot, doesn't engage – 'a shame when so intellectually capable'.

But she seeks *life*, questions how this stale room can be a part of the zoo; balks at the absurdity that slides are supposed to be a satisfying substitute for heartbeat and eye contact. The speaker drones. She cannot slow down to match his pace – her mind races, climbs, swings, trills; disinterested in what he has to say, his words the crunch of dead leaves, dust in the wind; oh this terrible attempt at theatre.

When lunch comes, she slips out nimbly, lithe; a reptilian retreat. She seeks a moment of existence distilled that will lift her from drudgery, just as the school hoped, but not in their exacting cube of institution. Though her agitation in class leads teachers to presume she has no patience, this is not true. She climbs a wall when no one is looking, hides among leaf laden boughs, and waits for a reticent feline shape.

She does not return to that airless room.

In her meditation, she breathes out gratitude that someone recognised her need.

The need to press her nose against the wild, to lament with those as trapped as she, those who thrum with the same caustic resentment towards their captors. The dappled cat flicks its tail, reveals to her its own tree branch hiding place. Their eyes lock; a song of suffocation passes back and forth.

They imagine a scintillating collage of damp jungles and grassy plains, of quiet woodlands and surging rivers. Freedom in its many guises. They breathe it in, and in some small way, slip from their bars.

When she breaks the jam jar, she sees herself
in every shard so she throws her face off the pier,
to sea-glass back to sand, soup into dolphins, be sea

Elisabeth Ingram Wallace
SUMMER 2020 SECOND PLACE

Tomorrow when they find their eyeballs on the floor, her parents will pick up the hacked photographs of their wedding album. Pieces of 1974 they thought were safe, high on a bookshelf. They will jigsaw, eye to face, around the kitchen table, holding glue-sticks. Their eyes will never look right again.

But tonight, the photographs are whole behind plastic, and eight-year-old Clem sock-foots past her parents' bedroom, stands on a chair; two figures, Twenty-one, Eighteen, outside a church. Everything is black and white.

~

Eighteen-year-old Clem is an artist. She builds a city out of bread. Then she photographs it as it decomposes.

She tries rye, wholegrain, spelt, but everything beautiful crumbles. In the end, she uses Mothers Pride plain loaf.

Along the way, she eats Grand Central Station.

Now when she shuts her eyes, she hears engines, trains running through her bones. In Tesco yesterday, she opened her mouth to say thank you to the cashier, and a loud honk came out, followed by the departures for the next hour, platforms 1–6, and Clem made sure to remind herself to step away from the platform edge.

~

At work, Clem, twenty-eight, gets used to referring to herself as a machine. Staff 'upload' information, 'share bandwidth.' Really, they all want to lie down on the floor, get drunk and cry.

With new management, staff are told to rank concerns – whether deadlines or a sexual assault in the car park – as Seal, Sea-Cow, or Polar-Bear.

The sea is nutrient soup. Humans must use mouths and digestive tracts, but some marine creatures can breathe life in through their skin, no stomachs required, every mammal evolves to survive. Manatee, walrus, sea-lion, porpoise, whale.

~

Two years after she becomes scared of her husband, Clem, thirty-eight, meets a woman once terrified of spiders before 'acclimatisation therapy'. The therapist made her carry a spider around in a jam jar, 'holes in the lid, to breath.'

'I might try that,' Clem says.

And she does. Jam-jars his toenail clippings, pubes.

Cuts holes in his T-shirts, each sock.

'Everything is falling apart,' he notices, near the end.

Now everything free smells like strawberry jam.

Delivery
Amy Barnes
SUMMER 2020 THIRD PLACE

I build brown caged skirts for Mother out of whale ribs and cast-off timber. Sister covers them in muslin, hiding our bird siblings, her nested-nether children not quite ready to survive on their own. As Mother's belly swells, we add petticoat after petticoat made from our own feathers.

Eventually, she can't fly to market or take us to school, instead sleeping upright bolstered by stiff skirts and growing still-egg-babies.

'Will the babies look like us?' we ask.

Sister points at my rouged belly. I bow my head in shame.

We are all hungry, but day-time food searches are dangerous. So, each night Sister and I fly the nest to dumpster dive food, snatch clothesline fabrics, stray newspapers, Christmas tinsel and fluffy dandelion cast-offs to cushion the babies and sustain Mother. Some nights, she cries in pain as the brood pushes on her back and steals her sleep, but it is for the best. She knows Father hovers, restrained by posted notices but ready to strike and hurt our unborn siblings. As the oldest, I take the night shift while he swoops for food from rooftops and treetops.

The days move forward as our tiny toes leave calligraphy snow-signatures. When the birth day comes, we watch as each baby pops out like nesting dolls falling into the soft leaves, straw and torn fabric we wove together. Mother rocks them all on the bloodied floor, her skirts still wet with birth.

We hear Father squawk-screaming and dive-bombing our safe sky home. He's hungry. Mother knows he can smell us from five hundred feet away, puffing out his sunburned chest as a warning. I gather more ribs and wood and create a protective iron bar quilt. She drops food in tilted-up mouths as Father flies overhead, looking for the cage's key.

Boots

Ariane Castelo Cipriano

It arrived on a Tuesday afternoon. I heard the postman placing it by the door. I pushed the box in with my foot and left it there.

I didn't say anything, although I was surprised at how quickly it arrived. You texted me asking about other things but really wanting me to tell you I'd opened the shoebox with your present.

That night, I dreamed someone was driving me somewhere.

The next morning, I felt no need to know what was in the box. I ate, I worked, I read.

I dreamed I'd just missed the bus.

The following day, you couldn't resist and asked. I said I had gotten the box. I didn't have time to open it, though.

You said it was meant to make me happy, so I took myself to the hall and looked at it. I saw the logo of a shoemaker on the side. I crouched and sniffed the brown tape around the package, then took it to my bedroom, feeling the weight of something heavy and small in the middle, and imagining things.

The car I wasn't driving almost crashed in that night's dream. I pulled the box closer before opening my eyes.

You didn't text. I sent you a song from the seventies and a picture of a cloud.

On the box, you wrote 'fragile' and 'please do not crush' in capitals.

I typed 'I'm overrun,' but you didn't want to know by what.

I placed the box upside down on my desk. You wrote 'do not drop,' imperative, below your first name.

I was hanging on the ceiling like a helium gas balloon, stuck.

From my bed, I saw the fine lines of a small pair of hiking boots drawn on a corner of the box.

I didn't eat or work or read. I waited.

I like to imagine you wandering up steep mountains or balancing on stones to cross a river.

Sometimes I read your last text: message me when you've opened the box. Then I look at the box on the shelf, its wrinkled tape across the front like a crooked ladder to unread stories.

The Blue Dress
Jenn Murray

Summer dedicated itself to a treasure hunt in the forest. My cousins and I would scour for gold. John, David and Aidan surrounded me in age. Mother trusted me. Aidan took a notion by the oak tree. His spade hit rock under the soft pull of muck, his cheeks red with exertion and focus. I was full from two cans of Coke, so I sat on my arse and watched the boys discover a chest the size of me if I folded in two. I rolled onto my knees. They joined me. Silent curiosity. Mounds of mud enveloped the groves in the wood.

Padlock.

David ran back to the farm for an axe.

'I'll do it.' John sliced the wood for the fires.

The padlock cracked like a beef bone. Aidan lifted the lid mightily. A knife, a notebook, a man's jacket and a pair of brogues. Underneath, a dress with a full skirt and petticoat. It mumbled dull red earth, but when I took it home and washed it, powder blue emerged. I laid a soaked flat person in the bath. The narrow waist was like my mother's. When I coaxed her upstairs and pointed to her younger self asleep in the bath, horror smacked her face.

'How?'

'Treasure hunt.'

'It's not yours.'

'Finders keepers.'

'No. Where is the rest?'

'We left the notebook in the chest. By the oak tree.'

I didn't mention the knife.

She fled from me. I heard the backdoor slam and her footsteps sweep through the long grass into the dense blackness of the trees holding tight the night.

Later my mother sat alone by the fire. From the doorway, I watched her burn one dirty old page after another, until all that was left was an empty spine and flame.

The Last Call of the Loon
Shannon Savvas

I remember Mum, camera out, concentrating on the framing or focusing while Dad and I pulled faces, heads together like a couple of loons. She'd get all sulky and snap, *come on, don't ruin it. Pair of bloody clowns.* After, we'd sit on the beach, or moor, or lakeside picnic grounds with a bucket of KFC, extra coleslaw for her, spicy for Dad and corn on the cob for me. Later, I'd explore, poke around the bracken or rock pools while they lay on a blanket. Canoodling, Gran called it.

On Boxing Days, out came the albums, cellophane cracked, yellowed and tacky. Dad fingered faded photos of himself at nineteen in harlequin-striped loons and body-hugging tees. *Look at those loons, sweetheart. Check out the hips and tackle,* he'd say with a nostalgic leer, patting his beer belly. But I knew he was happy to have that gut. Preferred it to the washboard and snake hips.

Years later, we'd spread the old snaps, remember sand in the KFC, ants in the picnic lemonade, his long-lost snake hips and ignore the dirty custard colour of his skin, his eyes, his fingernails and his enormous belly, tight with malignant fluid. *I'm a ghost of the man I used to be, sweetheart,* he'd say. We'd laugh. Mournful like loons at dusk. And though forbidden, he'd send me to the chippie. *Plenty of salt, sweetheart. My kidneys are fucked anyway,* he'd whisper.

Mum sat all night with his body in the front room before the funeral, singing his favourite songs. Her voice shrill, unable to find an octave, trembled like the call of a loon.

After we buried him, Mum refused to leave the kitchen. Wearing disposable catering gloves, she prepared trays of egg and cress sandwiches on white, ham and mustard on brown, scones and Madeira cake.

Always a bloody loon, ever since college, his best mate Bob sputtered at the funeral tea before going outside for a rollup. Only when Uncle Jimmy, tanked on beer and the last of Dad's single malt chasers, sat at the piano, did Mum find her octave for Dad's favourite song.

Ella Fitzgerald's *Lullaby of Birdland.*

Two Hearts
Bonnie Meekums

Two hearts beat in my chest. One lies hidden underneath the other, wings flapping in time, unseen, unheard.

Now, the top heart stays home, tucked safely in my body, while the other flies undetected across the globe, to another place far away. The stay-at-home heart pines silently for its twin. My chest becomes a ghost town. A town of ghosts. A dreamscape, where time and space have lost their way.

They tell me *this* is home. This is my *real* home. The one where the top heart lives.

It's where I learned to say, 'D'you wanna brew, love?' Where brew means tea. Not fermented crops, costing the earth and relationships. But forging bonds through shared hot water, steaming mugs. It's where I learned to walk up hills and still have breath to sing and shout. To twist. And shout. It's where I boiled nappies, scrubbed floors, and moved mountains on minutes of sleep.

Yes, this is home.

But then there's where my twin-heart flies, beating fast on wind to beckoning birdsong, on the cool night air where day is night and nights last forever. In that home, where proud mountain warriors stand guard round lake and town, I have no need to walk. I float through familiar streets. Invisible. Untouched. Longing to be touched. Yearning to be seen and turned to, hugged and argued with.

That's home.

Isn't it?

But then, I dare not stay.

My roaming heart is pulled back, bleeding, to its twin, where they beat in Steve Reich cross-rhythms, finding their way back to beat as one. One day, my hidden heart will have no need to fly.

Then. Then, I will know I am home.

Stardust Courage
Nicole Butcher

Ten minutes after I've arrived at the bus stop, the man in the bomber jacket musters the resolve to approach me. Not for the first time today, I long to be in my fifties, when my mother assures me that women gain the superpower of invisibility.

'You play sax?' He motions to the case I'm holding.

'It's a trumpet.'

He perseveres. 'You playing at the festival?'

Perhaps it's the line of stardust I just inhaled at the artists' bar that emboldens me to say yes.

Before I can backpedal, I'm elbow deep into a residency at the Silver Lining jazz bar in the Old Town. I contemplate bailing to buy chips, but my feet are wooden with cold, and the next bus could be another half hour away.

Then he says it.

'Play a tune while we wait?'

I curse Jake for asking me to take his trumpet home, and I curse Edinburgh for its cheap cocaine.

'Nah, sorry mate, I've clocked off.'

'Come on, it's depressing waiting for this bus. Cheer us up!'

Six or seven festival-goers now gaze at me, hatchling-eager, and somehow the prestige of the trumpet shrinks – its three valves seem insignificant in light of the four years of piano lessons I had in high school.

I valiantly press my lips to the mouthpiece, puff my cheeks and blow. The hiss of a sprinkle of saliva mingles with the wheeze and howl of traffic. Hopefully, this will pass for a warmup.

I reposition my mouth, close my eyes, and throw all my fifty kilos behind my exhale. The trumpet burps and buzzes. I push one valve, another, then all three. The pitch meanders flatulently around one note, then freefalls before my breath buckles, leaving me panting. The noise is reminiscent of a donkey being castrated.

Wiping spit from my mouth, I force my eyes open to discover an assortment of strangers buried in their smartphones – among them the back of a bomber jacket – and the astounding truth: I have found the key to invisibility at the prodigious age of twenty-eight.

The Almost Child
Jaz Hurford

It is no secret I yearn for you. At night, my mind draws pictures of you as a baby to find sleep. Crisp sunlight comes and I recall the images while your daddy and I lie there, not yet full of morning air. Giggle at the very joy of you; you all soft footed, all warm milk. He often indulges me a while, though his lips remain squeezed together in passionless embrace.

When you come to visit, I fry meat. Ordinarily, your father abhors such practice; normal mealtimes for us consist of bowls of lentils, of thanking the Lord. I lay three places at the table even in your absence, as though the silent silverware may summon a sudden knock at the door.

You always ring the telephone to announce arrival, though I gave you a key when you were just shy of ten years old. *It's open*, I holler loudly, as I shake water from the boiled vegetables.

And you step through, fresher than the new-found day. You uncork the wine; bottled the very year you were made. I plate our food as my head swills and spits out various greetings. Each one falters on my lower lip, tastes inadequate, somehow. Try as I might, I never have the words for you.

Thankfully, it seems age has weathered both our tongues. We eat without exchange. The silence is a gift inherited from him; the power to remain quiet even in uncomfortable places. But I know if conversation were possible, you'd tell me you're doing well. New job. Perhaps a child of your own on the way.

After
Sarah Leavesley

In my dreams, my husband feeds me strips of bread dipped in sunny yolk. Each time I bite, he loses a finger. Then his hand, arm, shoulder. Soon there's an egg-size hole in his heart. What's left pulses harder, faster. I push in my fist until the gap's wide enough for me to step through.

I dream this because dreams aren't real, because dreams defy the odds, because dreams can be forgotten. But even in these dreams, I patch myself with parts of him. Still, light oozes from the cracks. I try to hide this with smiles and bright words. I wash away my lost hair before he notices. Crows drink from my skin until their beaks turn yellow. I wake with black feathers in my mouth; he wakes with black feathers on his pillow. He can't see them, but he feels them. Life's a trance he can't control. Day after day, night after night, we both re-live my dying. He dreams me back with him. I try to dream things differently. Neither of us can escape, yet.

But next May, or the one after, when late sun makes everything glisten, he will lie back on the grass and realise the sky looks like an eggshell, protecting the world's softness. He will feel himself smiling, that smile more than just a daydream.

A week later, he will meet Bella at the café on the corner. They'll laugh at the strange serendipity of them both ordering a latte and eggs sunny side up. That night, he'll find a white feather in his pocket, unaware how recently I left it.

The Treacherous Hearth
Milly Yelf

It was toothpaste on the mirror which caught my attention, despite the fire warming through the hallway. If I could look past the splatter, I might have stood to appraise the flame eating its reflection. But then, once dutifully polished to a streak-free shine, I looked to the photos askew in the conservatory. The air was a dry mockery, a raspy chuckle.

I loved grain of the family portrait – clipped smiles of children – his cuff links – eyes wincing from the flash. But the seam of the old wallpaper was puckering from the heat, so I reached for a step ladder.

As I scraped the first sheet from its bindings, a handsome fireman hurtled through the backdoor. 'You need to leave now', he said, 'no time for faffing.'

'Oh hush!' The careful peel resembled the skin of my silver birch tree – aided by the happy heat. 'Hold me steady.'

He hesitated. Rocked on heels before lurching to clasp my ankles, the metal was too hot to touch. His fingers were steady and cool.

'You shouldn't be climbing on your own. You could break your neck.' He chastised as I eased the blackening paper from the wall with bare fingertips.

The frame of the bathroom mirror was melted five minutes prior. Clipped smiles – thirty seconds from consumption. My fireman's shoulders nipped by flames. The clock chimed, half seven.

'I've might have to go. I've got tea waiting.'

His dark eyes darted across the room. The doorway beautifully lit by waves of unalloyed heat. He opened the window to let some air in and slipped out the backdoor.

This may be a job for another day. Oh dear. And my scorched fingers skated over the TV – gathering dust as black as ash, and *I only just dusted this morning.* And *Oh God, the carpet!* But then, as I reached for the pink feather duster, he greeted me. Touch as airy as Sunday – leafy light.

There he was: a gaping vacuum of orange and blue, a pop, and a whiteness. Flames whipped across the underside of my earlobe with an indignant hiss, and yes, that also burned.

Buttercreep
Joyce Ann Wheatley

A mouse birthed and bedded babies where I would plant petunias. When my trowel blindly met her litter, my heart thudded over dirt.

I scooped them up and dumped them beside the compost, a ripe spot. I felt like a murderer, but you were coming, and a rodent nesting in my flower bed, my spot of peace and cultivation, posed risks to health and hygiene.

Beyond, the meadow grew deep and thick – knee-high, waist-high, chest-high, taller than you or I. I'd gather bluebells, forget-me-nots, ajuga, buttercups, dandelions, wild phlox and yellow mustard. I'd flutter over blossoms, like bumblebees and butterflies and all sorts of hummers, buzzers and stingers.

Until the dusk when Pan pranced in – Pan, fear-mongering trickster of twilight. It was Solstice night, and I'd just had time to relax when your father said, 'We shall have a lawn, like our neighbors.'

Forget-me-nots ought to have tangled his feet and tumbled him to ground, buried him in sky-blue petals, but his mower roared and rumbled. A gold-black butterfly, pollen-drunk and full of nectar, crept upon your Daddy's swath, and, on wild fields shorn, a mischief of mice squeaked along the border.

I tip-toed after them, under the split-rail fence, to a spot behind the oak where the neighbors rocked a swing, clinking ice cubes in their glasses and reading *Maisie the Mouse Plants a Garden* to their daughter, a little girl in pajamas, grasping after fireflies until the child closed her eyes and her parents carried her inside.

When you arrived, trailing your newborn wilderness, life smelled good and sometimes bad, but nature kept on growing. I met mice with careers and homes like you and me, and butterflies who descended from the sky to creep on fresh-cut grass.

John Dory All Summer
Barclay Rafferty

Are you sleeping, mate?

Bit scruffy out this morning. Take us an hour to get round the breakwater. Wait till you see the trawler. French-built. Plunders the seabed: monkfish, megrim, cuttlefish, a by-catch of all sorts, from turbot and brill, to pouting and ling. Seasonal, too. Used to drag Dad out in summer, plumb for John Dory. You'll do for now, though, if you're seaworthy, ready to graft.

Dad's in and out of hospital. Find myself doing the old agnostic prayer every time I get the phone call. Not much signal here, mind. Used to sneak in the wheelhouse, select autopilot, pretend he was in control, sort through fish: wash and gut them, coffin them in ice. Haul the cod-end aboard, empty nets, clear decks, flog treasure to local merchants, Michelin star Mayfair restaurants. Wonder if them fancy chefs can gut a basket of lemon sole in six minutes flat, eh?

Home by lunch, anyway...

You nodding off, mate? I do ramble. Shipping Forecast's like some old long-wave music box: *Hebrides, Dogger, Malin. Southeast gale 8 to storm 10, veering west. Thundery, squally showers, occasional icing. Moderate, becoming poor.* Reams of meteorological data, that. Crunched into three-hundred-and-fifty words.

Don't understand why folk listen. Unless you're bobbing about inshore, you've no idea what we're going through. Soon as they felt the howl in their lugholes, they'd paddle home quick-smart, without as much as a capsized wristwatch.

Fantasists. Always kept ghoulish hours, me. Kick-abouts till nightfall, cricket sight screens for boundaries. Ball on a piece of string. Could ping it, side-footed, forty yards, nutmeg a mermaid. Dad'd pick us up at dawn, 05:33 Forecast crackling in his old Cortina. Would close my eyes, imagine pitch waves, crashing foam, fathoms. Got me used to choppy waters, that.

Doze off a lot myself, mate. Dream of the old man lobbing fish back. Telltale sign is the wave packet. *Summer in that plaice yet*, he says. Anyway. National anthem at 01:00. I'll cannon out of bed in a stupor, salute the pips. Never heard the Greenwich Time Signal, mate? Know it when you hear it. Sounds like a heart-rate monitor, or some old machine reversing.

Sleepwalking
S Golden

Alone, she carries the wicker basket into ancient woodland and hums fragments of forgotten tunes.

For years, there has been a storm brewing. Low pressure sheds showers of doubt until she finds she is soaked in the spit of a man she once loved.

He consumes black morels and stropharia. He swears they never create gut ache for him. Over his appetites, he is unapologetic.

In recent months, she survived on scraps of fungi he brought home, detritus caught between nail and finger. He rarely bothers to return anymore, and when he does, he has scrubbed his nails until the quicks are raw and his cuticles are rough with synthetic compounds.

He sleeps, and most of their time together is spent in a state of unknowing.

She recalls lazy days of flesh-plumped dew. She tries to summon to mind early forages, those imperfect caps and gills with mottled skins whose mucked-up stems would propagate night after night.

How natural to see that waste created life.

One season they swell, the next they shrivel. Litter, like rot, spreads in sets of infection; one product blackens the other until all membranes turn to mush.

She hunts by the silvered light of old rooms, follows routes where they used to flourish in abundance. But all that is left are half-chewed plastic rings beneath the moon.

She crawls, poisoning hands and knees, digging into the mulch floor.

And she rakes over their remains in the hope that all of this festering matter will sprout morels that won't remember.

Contact Lenses
Rosaleen Lynch

Against this guy's advice, I leave my contact lenses in. I carry spares and glasses in a sealed plastic bag with my medi-kit and pre-packed lunch.

My glasses would fall off, I tell this guy I like, walking beside me, his secured with a strap behind his head. I'm afraid of not seeing, I say.

He says his fog up with heat and nervous sweat, and slips the tip of his bandanna under to wipe them, then slides his glasses up to nestle in his hair, as if they keep watch for him above the moving crowd.

I got my eyes checked late, I tell him. Thought everyone saw the same. As far as I could. It was a shock to know people saw more.

He says he was three when he got his first pair. Living his life within the frame since then.

I say corrective lenses showed me a whole new world, but I kept losing or dropping mine. I see much more with contact lenses. I have dailies, I say. Disposable.

He says he's had this pair of glasses for eleven years, he can't afford to lose or drop them. It's not a luxury people like him have, he says. And what about the planet?

Who are people like me, I want to ask this guy, but don't and wish I'd worn my glasses.

Later I tear at my contact lenses when the tear gas is trapped between them and my crying eyes.

Gong Show Night
Laurie B Holding

The survivor gets to tell the story. So hush.

It was supposed to be a fun night, my night out with the girls, the one night a month I could let my hair down, laugh 'til it hurt, drink all I wanted.

It was a gong show, hilarious. I dressed in one of your old black sports jackets and those stockings with the black line running up the backs that you used to like. I grabbed my dad's old fedora from the front closet, tucked my beat-up tap shoes into the duffle bag, kissed you without meaning to, so distracted, trying to remember the routine. Bette Midler's voice in my head.

And I kissed the kids. Them, I kissed with more than half a heart. Good thing.

I won! Me, who never wins anything. I won the freaking gong show. They tapped a keg as my prize and slapped thirty bucks into my palm. Lots of back-slapping, congrats, you still have great legs kind of thing.

You know the rest, you're tired of hearing about it, no doubt, too bad. Too damn bad. Telling you the story from my side of the window lets me hang on to this string of sanity another day.

I couldn't even pull up to the house. Neighbors in bathrobes, water spraying onto our brand-new roof. Water, everywhere, spraying from all directions. I found their rooms in the back, pissed myself standing there, watching the smoke. Did I see them at their windows?

Did I? Or am I making that up?

You ride a phantom shotgun in my new house, now.

I live in the Subaru.

Tap dance in front of the casino. People throw dollars into my dad's old fedora.

Days, I drive around with the smoky ghosts of my children. Tell you the story again.

With water spraying my cheeks.

Flesh and the Devil
Fiona J Mackintosh

At first sight of my leading man with his ink-black brows and the startling whites of his eyes, I remembered the lion.

Get in the cage, Greta, they said, it'll make a great picture. Behind the bars, the beast yawned, four yellow fangs and a gust of sour breath. It's more than my life's worth, I said, he'll smell the fur on my coat and rip me to shreds. Oh no, they said, he's a pussy cat. Wouldn't hurt a fly.

You remember how hard it is to be twenty years old. The ground's unsteady, your arms and legs have their own ideas. An on-the-edge, jiggery-pokery time of false bravado and too many feelings. Then imagine a long week at sea, walking the slanting decks, watching for the spires of a strange city to rise on the horizon. Then day after day on a train through a blur of prairies and mountains, people talking too fast in a language you barely understand. I already missed the gasp of cold on my face, the shine of the bay from the Strandvägen tram. I missed the *lussekatter* and the gingersnaps, the tinny steeple bells, and I missed Lena, her lips on my neck, my hands in the warmth under her skirt. Lena, who never answered my letters asking for forgiveness. And when at last I reached this place, the little man from the studio said, 'American men don't like fat women. And get your teeth fixed.'

So I did as I was told. I stepped into the stinking cage, palms sweating in my gloves. Though I smelled the jungle spirits on his breath as he looked my body up and down, I laid my head between his open jaws and nestled on the damp and juicy pillow of his tongue.

Urtica dioica
Abbi Harris

I have found myself walking more these days. *It helps to clear the head,* my mother would say. Nowhere in particular and always close to home, along familiar paths. I turn a corner, descending toward a small patch of woodland. An assortment of wild plants frames the periphery. But it is always the common stinging nettle that captures my interest – at first blush, a demure, unassuming plant. Unlike their gaudy, demanding counterparts – the red campions, the foxgloves, the clumps of sweet woodruff. It is the unpresuming thickets of serrated green eggs buried underneath, quite comfortable and self-assured enough to be in the shade of others.

I gingerly climb over the gate, nettles curling up in tendrils toward my feet. They do not seem to care that they are avoided, whether they are liked or not. I have always envied them for this; they are unashamedly themselves, nipping at the bare ankles of a child chasing summer in woodland or lacerating the paper-thin wrists of a grandfather tending his garden. They are somewhat akin to nature's botanical finger, its digit sprawling in flirtatious rebellion over graveyards and canal-paths. Perhaps this is their way of mocking us with cool indifference, feeding on us with a voracious, lusty appetite when our bodies are long gone, our bones buried.

Maybe it is this persistent preoccupation with those dull things that hide hidden depths, that led me to fall then. Tumbling into your bed. A sucker for a perennial, coy glance. Your embrace, a cool dark undergrowth climaxing in heady soil. Your tongue, a hit of sharp histamine. Tiny punches to the bloodstream through hollow hypodermic kisses. You are painful, but in the way that excites me.

Our union is momentary. I pick myself up and tentatively run my fingers over the places you touched, my lips, my thighs. Now swollen red welts.

Carnal badges, I think to myself. And continue walking. I reach home, and for the first time in a while, I find myself noticing the roses.

Cilla and Charybdis
Steven John

A whirlpool has appeared in the garden pond. The whirlpool roams across the surface of the water like the tornados over the American plains. As it sucks in air and waterborne detritus, it belches like soapy water draining from the bath.

I began by throwing in fragments of leaves from a pondside potted plant. I watched them glide towards the vortex, start to circle ever faster, closer and closer, until finally the flashes of green span down the silver spout like a shoal of tropical fish. I progressed to twigs and small dead branches fallen from a nearby tree. As my imaginary boats were pulled to their fate, I envisioned crews of mythical Greek sailors frantically rowing in the opposite direction as the mouth of Charybdis opened ever wider.

Since lockdown, Cilla has been stocking up on tongue, liver, and sweetbreads. I'm getting worried.

'I thought we were going veggie,' I said. 'Growing our own?'

'When in Rome,' she snarled and went online for stuffing recipes.

We were better at social distancing before, when we both left early and came back late. Sometimes now we're forced to eat in the same room, even at the same time. We wash and dry the dishes together, wearing tea-towels over our faces. In bed, we lie back to back to minimise risk of infection.

'It might be better if I make up the spare bed,' Cilla said.

This morning I took Charybdis a bacon sandwich and witnessed it being greedily devoured. Later, I sneaked a frozen leg of lamb. That too was gobbled up.

If I lie on the grass next to the garden pond, I can hear the call of bare-breasted sirens from where the spout funnels into the underworld. If I put my hand on the lips of Charybdis, I can feel the tug of her urgent kisses.

Youni
Kendoll

It won't stop.

So, show more.

Push yourself, you can't stop – dead the 'stop'.

Fuck expectations! No, don't dismiss them, spread-eagle to them. Let the man, behind the man, behind the man-bun, get behind you. Prove you've grown past the hill-rolls and greatly-exaggerated sexual-prowess of misguided youth.

Another cycle of emotionally-abusive 'woke' girls, all of whom study dance and something, and you've convinced yourself it's alright to be this sad. You're a burgeoning Art-Hoe, you need this.

Devote yourself to your breakdowns, they make you relatable.

You're your idols now. I mean, you kickbox now.

Now what? Next party? Yes, party. You spiralled, you're sprawled – cornershop-cider-upchuck-swirl in a toilet. You got dragged to it by some nice whoever. You hate it, you hate them. Uni kindness veers too close to self-righteous pity.

You get up.

More vom, fewer nutrients. A vision of making Girl X uncomfortable blindsides you. It's OK, guys like you weather these things – even called yourself a fuck-up and cried in front of her. Now you're just 'complicated', you can milk that for a while. It's Afternoon, thank god for Uber-eats. You order Vegan, you like how you talk when you mention you're vegan.

You've got lectures. You talk, a lot, think you know. Your lecturer sits you down, she says you're not terrible, just generic. You kill the urge to say generic and being an eight is less of a sin than fuggly and silent.

Second Year, first months: you know you'll be invited to Pre's, but some people have left you on READ for a while now... You get with a Fresher, a Fresher has friends. Salvation. You start again.

Signs of Life
Lindsey Booth

The bedroom radiator dinks and clanks as it cools. Relaxes into the shape it was before the heating came on. It doesn't look any different on the outside, hot or cold. But it must have been to make all that noise.

Anna doesn't remember her shape before Craig.

Outside looks much the same. A few more greys, maybe. Puffier under her eyes. But looks well, young even, for her age. All things considered. Things.

She runs palm over flat stomach. Drumskin taut across pelvis. 'You're so lucky!' Women say that. Women with muffin tops and weak bladders. Women with husbands and babies.

A foetus pushes aside organs, makes space inside its mother. Is born, grows, develops. From soft squashy face to hardened unique features. Behind it, an aftermath of stretch marks, weak pelvic floor, sleepless nights.

Anna's shape on the inside doesn't go back.

Dead husbands are scar tissue. Welts and hardened knots woven into widows' organs. Defined faces lose features, soften to impressions.

Anna carries him everywhere.

'I'm living for two,' she tells his side of the bed.

'Dink,' the radiator concurs.

Widows and mothers lie awake at night. Listening for signs of life.

Different Shades of Shame
Jennifer Riddalls

There are different shades of shame.

There's a yellowy shame, a bruise that's almost gone. You see those dandelion hues every time you kill time, wasting it away while it slowly kills you. Mustard-tinged spots blur your vision when pinching rolls of belly flab. Yellow is a shame born of vomit. You make yourself sick.

The worst shame is a livid plum-hued bruise, one you've worn since you were eleven. It's a sightless, silent shame that no one else has seen or heard. The colour comes from a memory – of the first time and that cheap, shiny, violet duvet. You focused on that material, the faux-silk of it and the noise it made, a scratchy rasping where the material had been snagged. Your head to the side, cheek pressed to the purple you pretended it was water, a sea of bright lavender. Once recalled, springing up unbidden, it sparks off a blistering shame that whispers; *you didn't say no, you didn't protest, you didn't even move.* You lay there, accepting, like the bloated purple starfish you once saw washed up on a beach. After #MeToo, all those years later, your shame deepened into the plum, because you knew you'd never confess. You're not one of the brave ones. Now you'll carry it forever, a hard chunk of crystallised amethyst that colours everything.

The kindest shame is blue. All different kinds of blue; a perfect cloudless sky after rain, a deep navy that allows the stars to sparkle, a cornflower pushing through the concrete. The heart of a bruise. It blooms when you create something good, something that couldn't exist without pushing on the bruised parts of yourself. Compensation. It reassures in cerulean whispers: *you're ok, you're fine.* And you really are.

The Physical Impossibility of Death
in the Mind of Someone Living
J T Sutlive

We ask, In what ways did he learn how to grip the knife? Was it you who taught the knots? Fairytales still use the threat of death to teach our children basic morals. We didn't need your son to become a tabloid reminder not to linger in the dark. Seven years until our Honor Students could wander lawns without our tiresome vigilance. And yet now you stand outside your front door and give us such khaki smiles. You claim that He Was Born A Holy Boy. We're owed the moral of this story: what within him changed? How did he inherit such violence?

She asks, How should we (could we) have foretold this outcome? He was churchbred, all shylike. Not a word when his father brought out the belt. At times at night, I'd even let him read his spaceship books. Those gave him an escape and an education. Later in his life, he'd wield such words with ease. And yet, look, he knew when work was work: with summer on his shoulders, he'd plant the pheromone traps across our tilled fields. Into the soil he'd half-bury these glass jars half-filled with chemicals. The lust-drawn June bugs would fall inside, and he'd close the lid to suffocate those little congregants. But once, oh: once I'd seen him open a jar and let a few fly out to God Knows Where. How could we predict this from a child with such Mercy in his blood?

He asks, How could I (should I) have forestalled this destiny? You ain't seen the shit I have. You ain't even got my eyes. As a pale-faced nobody, I'd look into those jars and see those beetles crawl over their kin's carcasses. Their sodden severed wings formed a kind of alien stained glass that blanketed the bottom. Whenever I held aloft a jar, a Holy light bled through that fucker. I confess I could see every atom of their woe. You'd be fools not to know that's how Our Good Lord sees us. And now y'all want to crucify me for trying to open that lid?

How Not to Fall Out of a Moving Vehicle
Rebecca Field

Don't ask him to slow down. Don't mention the speed limit. Don't touch the heating controls, wind down the windows or adjust your seat. This is not your car, and he doesn't want you touching anything. Don't remind him about the points on his licence, his community service commitments or his blood pressure (he doesn't like to be patronised, especially by you).

Don't give directions (unless asked), warn him about pedestrian crossings or check the wing mirrors when he makes a turning – you are not the driver here; he is. Don't grip the sides of your seat as you swerve around corners or slam your feet into the floor as your approach a junction. Don't shrink back into your seat, screw shut your eyes and pray for a police car to appear. Don't scream there's no room to overtake, there's a bend up ahead, there's a cyclist on the other side – he can make it because he can drive properly and he knows what this car can do and he doesn't need you distracting him.

Don't say that his driving makes you nervous (an understatement that assumes he cares about how you feel). Don't cry or whimper or sniffle; that only makes him angry. Don't ask if he will let you out at the traffic lights, undo your seatbelt, open the door as the lights turn red. Don't get into his car in the first place when you know what he gets like. Don't do that, because then it will all be your fault.

Hung Up
Jenn Linning

I have been inside you. I know your shape, the feel of your touch. I cannot unknow it now, though I often wish to.

Your rough hands with their frayed edges caressed my throat. Marks of your grip still linger now: scratches, cuts, one slight burn. You nearly had me.

Funny: you made me feel so close to death, yet so inescapably alive. An unwelcome euphoria washed over me in your presence.

Your manner and your scent told me you had done this before. I thought you had saved yourself just for me. But no. Someone else had been inside you, felt suffocated by that same possessive grip. I could sense them: their very soul lingered in that space.

My hands were tied; I was blind. Powerless to resist. I hung on your every movement, knowing that at any minute, you might choose to end my life. Tighten your grip further, squeeze my throat, slow my breath, pull the rug from underneath me, watch me fall. The ultimate punishment.

But it was not to be. Not my time. Not my crime to pay for. Someone realised their mistake just before the lever. The vultures were not impressed. Deprived of death, they shrieked for blood. Demanded it.

I've come to watch you finish it this time. I had to see you again. Morbid curiosity, they would probably say. I glimpse your new victim as he is thrust roughly into your embrace. You grasp his throat, and I feel sick with envy. I know what he feels right now. That strange euphoria is difficult to recreate. Believe me: I've tried. It's just not the same without you.

Nobody halts the lever this time. In one deadly movement, the floor is snatched from under the criminal's feet. He drops like a stone (he's heavy, far heavier than I), but you're ready. You catch him with such suddenness and strength that his head snaps back and his neck breaks immediately.

As the crowd gasps and falls silent, I hide a smile. You are clearly having fun. You swing back and forth, ecstatic to have fulfilled your purpose. I try to be happy for you.

The Things We Left Behind
Amy Lord

We met under grey-blue Midwest skies, shouldering backpacks from the Greyhound stop to a diner across the street. Ate blueberry pancakes at noon and talked about the things we left behind.

You shared a photo of your brother, taken months before his overdose. He wore a football jersey, grinned wide for the camera, no idea he was about to blow his knee out on the field. The pain prescription would be the beginning of the end.

I laid a map out on the Formica table, traced the route I was taking, fingertip tender on the small black dot that marked my birth mother's home town. The row with my adoptive parents sat heavy in my heart.

A red-haired waitress brought us more coffee, let us talk until after dark. She perched on a stool behind the counter, reading a Bukowski novel, the yellowed cover folded back, silver bracelets jangling each time she turned a page.

The fairground across the street closed at midnight. One by one, we watched the neon lights extinguished. An exhausted manager secured the gates and walked towards home, trailing his cap along the railings.

The door chimed as we left the diner. You lit a cigarette beneath the streetlight, took my hand while you smoked it. Main Street was silent; a scene from Hopper's painting.

Laughing, we ran across the street and scaled the fence. I was a ghost in a white dress, running through the empty lot.

You turned on the lights for deserted rides; we danced to music from the carousel. I've never stopped spinning.

A guard came. His shout rang across the abandoned park. We broke apart beneath the Ferris wheel, running in opposite directions. I crawled through a gap in the fence, snagging my rucksack on the torn metal. You were a shadow scaling the motionless ride as the guard swung his torch into every corner.

At dawn, I waited by the bus stop, ready to start a new journey together.

Blue lights flashed outside the fairground gates. A deputy unrolled police tape across the entrance as his radio crackled: 'One male, deceased. Body's by the Big Wheel. Looks like he fell.'

Red Ochre Rising
Dettra Rose

I'm roadkill on red earth. Car is three metres away, wheels in the air.

Outback stars powder the blackcurrant sky.

My mouth's a ridge of broken teeth and my leg dead as butcher's meat.

Feral pigs and dingoes howl in the heartbeat of the night. I'm dinner on a dirt road plate.

My wife's asleep at home, but I see her here in the emptiness. Hear her.

'Don't drive all that way. Fly.'

Didn't listen. Never do, she'd say.

Minutes pass. Hours. Weeks. I don't know; time is lost and broken.

I holler at a passing truck, but wheels spit grit and the driver's blind to me. It shrinks to a dot. I whimper.

Hazy apricot sunrise, sweat beading down my back. One dim headlight pulls up. Pile of guys dark as charcoal stand over me.

'What happened, brother?'

I point to my leg. To my tumbled four-by-four.

'You had a wobble-up. You'll be right.'

'Am-bu-lance,' I croak.

'Out of range, bro.'

They raise me clumsily, slide my flesh into their tray-top ute. I'm next to a mottled cattle dog.

'He's friendly, don't worry.'

Dog slobbers me, tongue warm and meaty.

Engine starts, sounds like a screeching bat. Sheets of pain hammer my leg and privates. Guy hops in the back with me and the hound.

'Hospital's not too far, bro. We'll speed all the way.'

He rests his hand on my shoulder.

I half lift my index finger and point to the dawn. Sun ball to the left. Moon ball to the right. The sky is stoking an amber fire. Not many people die watching something as pretty.

'Our mob's name for sun is Walu. She's decorating herself with red ochre right now. After Walu lights a stringybark tree, carries it west across the sky. So bright it lights up country. When she stumps it out, daytime's finished.'

'The sun is a woman?'

'Old lady.'

I imagine her. Old sun lady, soaring torch of flames. Sparks crackling. Embers in her skin. Hair blazing. Eyes seven shades of fire. One is the startling red at emergency.

A Piteraq Is an Avalanche of Wind
Sara Hills

When Bellamy first tastes the power of the wind, she's six. She crouches in the closet, her parents curling around her like a shield. Outside, the wind uproots the copse of silvery-blue pines. It chews the chinquapin oak in half and hurls the green canopy, Bellamy's tire swing and all, through the window and onto the faded blue carpet.

At age eight, the shutters bang like gunshots. Mama says it's only the wind, but the sound penetrates. It enters the house, shouting and cursing up the stairwell. It shakes the hinges on the front door, shaking Mama out with it.

At twelve, Bellamy studies the winds of the world, searching for clues about Mama. Whenever Dad talks of her, his tongue flakes with ice, like the Bise, Tramontana, and Mistral – the chill-bringing winds of Europe.

Bellamy sleeps with the window cracked, reciting the names of winds like sheep in the stony silence. She stops at Wreckhouse, wondering if the wind that took Mama had a name like that.

At fourteen, Bellamy finds a hidden polaroid of Mama, mouth loose and bare back arched like a sapling in a fresh gale. In the mirror, Bellamy traces her own contours, mimicking Mama's bend and sway. Bellamy wets her lips and recites the heat-bringing winds like an incantation – Leste, Foehn, Sirocco.

At fifteen, her father comes home early and finds Bellamy with a boy between her legs. Her father's cheeks redden and puff, anger swelling like a piteraq, an avalanche of wind. Bellamy crouches on the floor, curling her hands around herself like a shield.

At sixteen, Bellamy folds gum wrappers into pinwheels and welcomes boys through her open window. Together, they rattle the windowpanes and climax like gunshots.

When her father asks, Bellamy tells him it was only the wind. It doesn't feel like lying.

At seventeen, she stands at the mirror and traces her contours, cradling the arc and swell of her changing form while the air stirs inside her, fluttering, soft as a zephyr.

Bellamy packs a bag, and when the wind picks up, she's gone – Mama's polaroid in her back pocket like a destination.

My Mother Didn't Rock Me
Barbara Kuessner Hughes

The ocean did. Jacintha didn't sing me lullabies; her cigarillo-sanded voice rasped out sea shanties in tranquil lagoons. My bathtub was the surf. I lay in the shallows, stroked to and fro by the tide.

Round and round the Pacific we sailed, our timber yacht a speck beneath the dwarfing sapphire heavens. My nightmares are about storms; many times, the sea nearly ate us.

Jacintha had unanchored herself from family ties and my landlubber question-mark father. I don't know why.

I was an amphibian with tanned human skin. Palm trees were my climbing frames. The waves dandled me, my legs dangling over the bowsprit.

When I was five, Jacintha would say, 'You make dinner, Timothy.' I teetered on a stool in the galley, fought tins open, concocting sludges which I found delicious, melting ravioli, oxtail and Marmite, or peaches, rice pudding and cheese. I harpooned fish, grilled them in the star-pricked obliterating night.

Jacintha made me literate and numerate, taught me geography and navigation, and wrote the book which made her famous.

When I was eleven, she said, 'Time you went to school.'

School in England was a catastrophic loss of motion and light.

Meanwhile, Jacintha learned to design boats. Her draughtswomanship, pre-software days, was as outstanding as her sailing and authorship, her vessels exemplars of shark-like efficiency. I study her forceful inky lines, and they're 3D. I'm on that creaking deck again, her eagle's face intent, powerful weathered hand on the tiller.

When I was sixteen, she left for the Caribbean. I receive an occasional email.

Do I blame Jacintha for anything? Not really. She loved me in her own craggy way. As for me? Affection and veneration are separate streams. But she gave me hardiness and freedom. I've used my freedom to moor myself.

My cottage overlooks the freezing basalt sea. I work in a boatyard, teach children to swim. My wife embraces me. My sons catch food in a supermarket. In their aquarium Neon Tetras shimmer and dart like the undersea gems which I chased over coral. I try not to look at them, try to forget how far I am from that swathe of blue.

Beetle
Sam Payne

I wake to find a forest growing in the corner of the bedroom. Tender green saplings pushing up through the floorboards, lengthening and thickening to bark. Branches twisting and spreading beneath the ceiling, their leaves unfurling in the moonlight.

Next to me, Jacob is snoring, his half of the bed sunken with the heft of him. Even in sleep, his body is rigid, his gnarled features are rooted firmly in a frown, and I wonder what kind of dreams are enraging him.

The room fills with the scent of damp wood and decay. A beetle, black and shiny, scuttles over the bed. I pick it up and put it in my mouth. When prey is scared, it stays still, hoping to fool the predator into thinking it is dead. The weight of the not dead beetle is an acorn on my tongue.

Beside me, Jacob shifts and groans. My heart clenches and bucks against the cage of my ribs. If he wakes, he will blame me for the forest. This is just how it is. I spit the beetle into my palm and place it on the bed. It scurries away, and I envy its instinct.

Ivy weaves around the trunks of the trees, looping over the branches and reaching out into the bedroom. Veined leaves probing and tangling around the legs of the bed. I close my eyes and try to sleep. But only lightly, in case the ivy decides to strangle me in what's left of the night.

Autocomplete
Jordan Harrison-Twist

We are in bed together, and I crack the window to let in some air, cool as a spoon. I hear vagrant talk, a woman shouting in the telephone box, and I fill the spaces shot through it by the wind. *Childcare* [is, surely, a collaborative] *enterprise* [but quite frankly, you have been distant, absent, even] *mind* [and body. You once would enjoy taking me against the french doors and delight at the neighbours, cooking eggs, who would catch my pink bare bottom pressed flat against the glass]. *Now the* [darkened bed stretches before us to stage our fantasies of infidelity and now I] *do not think* [my bottom could ever really be pressed flat again]. *We* [sit there and shake our heads when she is bidden stay in the hotel room, put on the dress which will arrive at the door, and wait for my return; but did you notice as you once noticed the smile as she waits and she takes down the zip, slips in her pointed toes; but did you notice there was nothing workaday in the silk? Did you notice the frenzy of the coming and the never coming back?] *So I am going* [away, a tireless lightless galleon] *until* [I forget the promise of age's palindrome and I forget you in your headset shooting teenagers on screens].

I want to reach out to the dear girl and say that everything will be better soon. I get back in bed, click the lamp, and light a cigarette which I know you despise.

A Far Fall
Kelly Griffiths

You, at the roof's edge. Me, noiseless. Step. Step. Step. Your T-shirt tents your shoulder blades. I want to brush my fingers along the delicious ridge of your tanned arms – without permission like the woman who stole a healing from Jesus. I want brazen hands to rake your hair and bold lips to kiss you.

Being an eighth-grade girl, a dandelion, not enough cheek or chest, I push you from me. From behind, so you don't see it coming.

It was supposed to be a joke: my hands' rough grasp on your shoulders. My thought was to drive you over the edge and yank back before you fell. I wanted to scare you. You'd laugh in relief, maybe pretend to be mad so you could take my arms as I'd done with yours. Maybe you'd even shake me and ask what the hell was I thinking. You'd cinch me to you. I'd feel your breath, your pounding still-spooked heartbeat. Together, our fear would become euphoria. We, the rush. I, the alchemist.

I jolted you, thinking you'd kiss me. Really. That was the plan. I know it doesn't make sense now. But I thought, a little recklessness? I could grab your shirt if I had to.

And I *was* able to pull you right back. We laughed. You were scared. Like a runner at the finish line, you hunched over and grabbed your thighs and gulped air. Your wide, unbelieving eyes said you thought I was crazy.

It worked, though, the recklessness. You kissed me.

Years later, you're at the edge again, on a roof of sorts but much, much higher. Your back, broadened by sweat and consequence, stretches and scallops your button-down shirt. Your steel-toed work boots kick ass daily. Nothing scares you now.

Thinking it'll be like last time, I come at you from behind, shove with mostly playful intentions. Now it's me, on the edge. You are far below. I pushed a little harder. My reflexes aren't what they once were. When the shirt ripped, your arms spread wide but didn't turn into wings.

I've had such a far fall onto this rooftop.

Spines and Tiny Hearts
Rupert Dastur

Last week, we cleared the garden of the old year: all of it piled up at the back. It had dried out under the sun and caught quickly, the flames spreading. I felt its heat and watched the smoke rise. I thought of ghosts and prayers.

'Daddy!' shouted my son, running towards me. Seven years old with wide eyes, his lips quivered as he pointed to the burning mass.

'You've murdered them!' he cried.

Confused, I reached towards him, but he shook me off.

'That's where they live,' he said. His eyes waxed, and his nose streamed as if his whole body was expelling something vile of which I was the cause.

'It's where the hedgehogs *hibernate*,' he explained.

It was a new word. I could picture him sitting at his desk, carefully copying the letters.

I had no idea if there are creatures protected beneath that dense pyre of leaves and roots. It was quite possible. I weighed the tears of my little boy.

'It's okay,' I told him. 'There wasn't anything living there.'

'Are you sure?' he asked.

He wanted to believe me. So young, and yet already he was beginning to see through the cracks of parenthood. I wished his mum was alive. I'd always said she'd be okay.

I told him that I had rustled the great mountain, that I searched for entrances and exits and found none.

It wasn't long before he was running around, laughing at things seen and unseen. At ghosts, perhaps.

I almost feel as if I've been let off. But then, at times, I catch him looking at me when we're in the car or sitting down for dinner, and his eyes are so serious that I wonder.

Yesterday, we were watching his favourite cartoon and he turned to me and said, 'Daddy, imagine if someone burnt our house down.'

I told him no one would ever, ever do such a horrible thing. And he looked at me and shrugged, and I had no idea, no idea what that shrug might mean.

Last night I dreamt of hedgehogs, curled up, spines on the outside, their tiny hearts protected.

Populus tremuloides
Iona Winter

Through the sliver of your bathroom window, I can see the entire beach. At night I hear the ocean calling to me, but I'm stuck here, within sight but unable to touch. The slap-slap-slap of tī kōuka leaves in the breeze, and the lowing of cows both soothes and unsettles me. All of my nerve endings are firing. Nothing's prepared us for this.

~

Fuck, it's a crack up listening to women talking about the run on toilet paper in the supermarket while we wait to grace the surgeon with our presence. And how, when they were kids, they used newspaper.

'Harden up, buttercup,' one of them says to her mother when she returns teary-eyed after seeing him.

I sit and listen to their litany of body dysmorphic shit, while part of me wants to scream, 'I don't care what size you are 'cos you're alive, aren't you?'

~

Sunrise stains your curtains, where before there was an absence of colour. I lost the black coral heart you gave me. Yesterday, your sister's hapū belly was so lush I could feel it. I dreamt I followed a trail of bloodied tissues along a track, where stripped bark and the broken walls of a long-abandoned garden guided me. Pain has the power to become all-encompassing. I stood beneath a *Populus tremuloides* and marvelled at the way its leaves quivered without judgement. Then I lifted my face to ingest the lick of falling leaves and willed my tears to come.

Picnic of Champions
Kate Ciolkowski-Winters

He sets up the blanket next to me, performing a delicate dance so as not to upset the wind before securing all four corners on the ground. A silly little man. Why in God's name would he ever want to put a buffer – a silky, flowery, mass-produced buffer – between himself and this beautiful *Earth?*

My middle school English teacher hammered 'nothing gold can stay' into my muddy brain that's now hardened like clay. Of all the beautiful vases, magical flutes, and foundational bricks my mind could have become, it's been relegated to forever take the shape of an elementary pinch pot.

Smooth Out The Edges
NOTHING
Roll Your Clay Into A Ball
GOLD
Stick Your Thumb In The Middle
CAN
Pinch All Around
STAY

Nothing gold can stay, have you heard? Not a pretty sunset, not a wonderfully euphoric moment, not sand in your hands; it slips right through. Gold, it's gold! This sand is fucking gold, and he wants to sit on his mother's tablecloth.

Maybe it reminds him of that time she forgot about the chicken in the oven. Its wings were so deformed one could take a single glance and lament the very existence of the chicken in the first place, assuming its lifelong inability to fly. That was the night she finally acquiesced to breakfast for dinner. He scarfed down three bowls of Lucky Charms. Good choice. OR maybe it reminded him of that fateful meal in which he was informed of his parents' separation over Mom's Famous Lasagna. The steam of the dish masked the tears of his mother across the table and produced the sweat on his father's brow.

Looking over at him again, I find that his delicate dance I found so delightfully charming has suddenly devolved into an angry jig. I watch as he runs manically from corner to corner, cursing each fold and wrinkle the wind forces into the blanket, mystifying the shapes of the lilacs and lilies that reside.

'Waffles?' I ask

'Sure, fuck this.'

Act of Contrition
Ashley Jeffalone

He can't sit in the confessional anymore, can't divulge what makes him wicked as another man watches. He'll go, and he'll try, but the evil stops on the wet of his lips; his knees ache to unbend, or snap. He'd go if he could, for the feeling afterwards is something else: relief, richer than relief, an ascent, heretical. The absence of air in his breast. I like the way it sounds. I like how he says it. He looks at me when he mouths the word *sin*.

He won't go to the confessional, but he'll stroke my wrist when he tells me about the words in his mind, how they grow dark and voluminous and rot in his throat. He doesn't dare grant them the curves of his tongue, but the shape of them tempts him. *Temptation's like smoke.* When he brushes my shoulder with the pad of his thumb, he tells me he'd like if I'd come meet his kids. They drive him mad with their clumsiness, how long they sleep in, how that sleep keeps their eyes closed; they don't look at him. If I were his wife, if I were his child, I'd wake up before dawn and balance plates on my palms.

He hasn't gone to the confessional or even to church, but he comes to the parking lot to relish the bells. Long withdrawn from the pews, *brimming with evil*, he says his lust sends him careening into my hands. After mass, I hold him – my fingers are chaste – and whisper *you are forgiven. I forgive you.* But I can't reconcile his sins like the Lord. He shrugs off my touch and drives home to his wife.

He goes back to the confessional, and I don't see him for weeks. But one day, he comes to me and tells me the truth: some days, he grows so hot with rage that he's afraid of his hands. Sometimes he grows so dull with apathy that he's scared he'll act. I stop waiting in the church parking lot and close my eyes to him. And I think, perhaps, forgiveness means nothing at all.

A Horse That Kicks Backwards
J A Keogh

And I know that it's not fashionable to write letters anymore, but then I never really wanted to be hip. And I know that snail mail won't ping your inbox or answer your string of blue message bubbles. But I'm going to try and explain what I couldn't explain.

It definitely wasn't the way that you held my hand that whole year when I was scared to go out in shoes. It couldn't have been your angular late-period Picasso features which contradicted your rougher edges. I really liked them. It wasn't when your mother detonated at our engagement, depositing a fine layer of national disaster grey over us, either.

It may have been when you painted the nursery a masculine marmite. Then afterwards sold the cot because everything happens for a reason. Even though it never does. Maybe it was the penny drop: your potential was infused with narcotic. The buzz that made you strange and unpredictable, like a horse that kicks backwards.

It was probably that stonewashed denim iceberg that prodded a hole in our fragile vessel. We started taking in water: my leaking tears versus your dripping fluids. You hastily built a liferaft out of hope and nostalgia but it was only big enough for one. And then you panicked, turning the house back to front, but you still couldn't find the distress flare. And you would never agree that it was always women and children first.

Dysmorphia
Alison Woodhouse

'Don't forget to remove your clothes. You won't be needing them anymore.' The receptionist smiles, razor-bone cheeks pointing the way.

Behind the curtain, I fold the lumberjack shirt, still redolent of my dad's tobacco smoke; my skirt made from nursery curtains, unused for their primary purpose, as things turned out; my greying bra; black pants. *Thanks*, I whisper, because I know the importance of gratitude, and step into the glass cubicle.

I face the mirrors. Fat rolls on my back, my belly hanging low, red spider veins on my dimpled thighs, breasts so heavy my husband requires both hands to cup just one. I am an awesome sight. There's so much of me, I barely fit their box.

I rattle the plastic pot, the sort you pee into for the annual check. This magic pill, the size of a pea, will recalibrate me to an appropriate size, as judged by the health management programme. It will poison the taste of my guilty pleasures; blueberry muffins, chocolate ice-cream, hot buttered toast. I will step from the box as skinny as the receptionist.

The next client is already here, her pen signing away a fortune. I recognise her apologetic giggle and shuffling feet, her shame, the shame, always the same. I haven't told anyone what I've done, for fear they'll say what's the point, you burst your gastric band, why waste more money?

Why indeed?

I punch the button, and the door slides open. I yank back the curtain and stand there in all my glory. The next client, even more magnificent than me, drops the pen. I pick it up, shake my head and open my arms like a diva at the end of the opera, waiting for the roses. She laughs, a rich, honeyed tone, and we fist bump like compadres.

I head towards the exit. Who needs clothes? I've got body armour on, kilos of it, but the skinny receptionist is there, trying to stop me.

'Does this pill work in reverse?' I ask, popping it in her mouth, watching as her eyes widen when the taste of pleasure floods back and those razor-bone cheeks become less certain.

Milk and Medusa
Michael Handrick

She takes my hand, presses it against hers and closes our fingers together. Strangely, this act seems the most intimate. Not the time she first kissed me, on an unfinished bridge in Avignon with the Mistral blowing around us and the lingering taste of cherry ChapStick. Not the time she held me, as I cried, and coiled my hair to form little golden whirlpools across my scalp. Not the time she held ice against my cheek the first time it happened.

The patio doors are open, and the wind is warm. The bowl is still on the table and flies flit into the milk's surface. She had torn off the crusts and dipped the bread in it. Fed me piece by piece. I winced every time I chewed. The white dripped down my lips. White as the moon, red as blood. Like the womb that made me, the breast that fed me. The same colours I won't be able to give.

Our skin sticks together; bodies curled like one big question mark. The question mark that forms whenever we're seen on the street together. It was in this room where that question was solved. Where my body made sense. Outside, my other body is an alternative fact. Inside, that question mark now grows bigger.

The silence between us deepens, the mint on her breath fades, the milk on mine sours. I trace the snakes on her Medusa tattoo with my finger and wonder when it will calcify my body.

I Am a Rock
Sadie Nott

I am a rock, Dad would sing, all jazz hands and hippy hair, bacon sizzling in the background.

In the next line, he was an island. A tropical island with gibbons and parrots and emerald leaves. With sand for sandcastles and pirates for adventure.

He sang about building a fortress. It wasn't a fortress to keep you out. It was a fortress that protected, like the arms of a bear.

Robert the Rock, Mum called him because of the song. Everyone else called him Bob. A bob was a shilling in old money, a shiny thing in your hand on a Saturday. When the quicksand days came, I had my hair cut into a bob.

His middle name was Thomas. RT. Arty. Magically, his initials were him. He painted many things, but mostly he painted rocks. Cliff faces, the faces in cliffs, rocky shores and rock pools, back when we lived on the coast. After he moved to the edge of the moor, the rocks he painted were tors. Stone-stack sentinels keeping watch from on high.

He was a consoler. In his days of dying, his phoneline words were I'm halfway better.

When all that was left of him were grey flakes, I scoured his painting journal. Sixty years of calligraphy, the tale-telling titles of each rock he had painted. I made a tally to find out which tor he had painted the most.

In the raw April winds, we climbed the moor's slopes. Up and up. Clamber, scramble, cry. Two auburn ponies gazed at us, still as stone, their manes blowing in the furious wind. At the top of Dad's most painted tor, rooted between the boulders, was a waist-high tree sculpted by the moorland gales.

We stood by the tree and tipped Robert the Rock into the arms of the air. When it was my turn, a riptide gusted flecks of him onto my face, into my open mouth. Tiny parts of him lay on my tongue, like grit, like snowflakes. I paused. I swallowed.

A tiny part of me is rock.

Remember.

After the Bowl of Raspberries
Pam Morrison

She draws her finger over the frayed piping on the green sofa, focused and slow, like a sleek violinist, drawing her bow in a rising glissando. But that would have put her on stage, in a straight-backed polished wood chair, not on her knees, as we find her. Her chin is stained with raspberry juice, a treat she'd been planning ever since the lock-down order came through on the news. Isolation consolation.

Those rhyming syllables and the rushing sweetness of sated anticipation had prompted, just minutes ago, an upwelling of gratitude. Out it poured, with Italian accent and operatic flounce: head back, throat open, her own spontaneous song in unabashed vibrato, her body spinning a pirouette that would have amazed her dead husband.

It was a saying she'd heard way back, and at last, she was doing it: dance like no-one's watching and sing like no-one's listening. There was no intake of breath when she saw the sitting room take a lean. The fall she'd been avoiding all these months finally had her in its arms. How strange: the way time slows down as if to catch you, she thought on her way down.

Her hip burns as she rotates onto her knees. There is no-one to call.

She surrenders. She remembers the slender woman with jet black hair, first violinist, Czech orchestra, 1981. She draws her finger along the frayed piping on her green sofa. Albinoni, Adagio. Angel. She is alone. Whatever happens, she thinks, I will be alright.

Mouse
Gillian O'Shaughnessy
AUTUMN 2020 FIRST PLACE

Grandma ate poison five times before it killed her. It was hard to keep it down, but she persisted. She went mad, they said, because of the isolation, she couldn't hack it, she was a city girl after all, an intellectual, she came to life at parties, she smoked and wore high-neck lace dresses and polished button boots, she danced with slick suit boys, not third sons out riding the boundaries checking the fences for months and months.

She ate the shouting in her head; she ate her shrieking heart. She ate the crashing silence of the endless outside, with only the grizzle of grey-backed sheep and the whine of flies for relief. On bad days she'd walk miles to the top of the long dirt driveway and back again, to the hot dust that turned her sheets and dresses brown and the ochre-coloured everything that stretched for days and days.

She ate the loneliness she wasn't meant to notice. She ate boredom straight from the packet and stopped remembering why she really should get a plate. No-one to care if she did or she didn't. No-one to drink gin with on the verandah. No-one to discuss the newspapers that came months too late, just a mirror of drab women with blank faces she saw once a year at shearing time when they came to help with the cooking for hours and hours.

Grandma ate poison five times before it killed her. Some women would do that before they'd leave their husbands and their children because if there is too much of you, if you can't swallow your panic that this is everything there'll ever be, all you can do, all there is to do, is become smaller and smaller.

She didn't leave a note. But I know.

The Bad Baby
Louise Watts
AUTUMN 2020 SECOND PLACE

I buy a card because my mother has broken her hand. The card has an elephant on it in black and white, and in the elephant's trunk, a bunch of flowers in colour. I do not buy the card because it was the least worst card in the supermarket. I buy the card because I have a memory of my mother reading me *The Elephant and the Bad Baby* inside me like a doughnut, like a potato, like an unfurling fist, like a flower. She used to read me *The Elephant and the Bad Baby*, and I would say 'please!' because the bad baby never once said please. Please, I would say, please.

Do you have a stamp? I ask my husband. Either he does not reply, or I do not hear him reply. Do you have a *stamp*? I ask my husband.

At night, I wake, and I think of the two bones broken in my mother's wrist. I think of them about the length and breadth of bird's legs. I think of them broken near the top, and I can see the gap where they do not join up anymore. I think about growing old.

When I last visited her, we sat in the garden. She put mealworms on the garden table, and I could hear a fluttering everywhere around us in the bushes, near but unseen. She called the bird like the remembered chickens of her childhood, *chit, chit, chit.*

Come now, she said. Come. Eat.

The bad baby ate a lollipop and a bun and a pie and an ice-cream and never once said please. The baby only said please when it wanted to go home.

I want to go home. Please, the baby said. Please.

An Apology, of Sorts, to My Brother at His Funeral
Diane D Gillette

AUTUMN 2020 THIRD PLACE

Let's say we grew up with parents who loved each other. Let's say that we don't both know that Mom should've packed you up and made her escape long before I was born. Let's say you don't resent me for that. You don't resent me for coming onto the scene in the most untimely of ways, the ultimate pain in your rear that you'd never be able to slide away from. A baby sister. The trap that held us all there.

Let's say we played checkers, and sometimes you let me win. Let's say the board never got flipped in a huff. Hard to say which one of us that wasn't. Let's say that we did the dishes together after dinner, and there were no such things as girl chores and boy chores, that my hands could push the lawnmower as easily as yours could dry the dishes. Let's say the punishments were divvied up equally, and you were never whipped with the certainty that you weren't as loved as me. The swish of the fishing pole whipping through the air as it found your bare flesh never happened. Let's just say that. Let's pretend you don't blame me. Let's pretend I don't either.

Let's say we both remember the blue skies more than the midnight black. Let's say we're sitting on our lawn right now. It's Labor Day. The sun is barely up. Our shoulders and noses are peeling from a summer spent racing down waterslides headfirst, and school doesn't start until tomorrow, and we are in denial that summer will ever end. Let's say there are hot air balloons peppering the sky, and this is one of those magical years when the wind is just right, and they will drift over our house, scaring the shit out of the dog and delighting us like nothing else ever could. Let's say there are enough strawberry toaster pastries for both of us, but we share one bottle of orange juice, and you don't mind my cooties for once. Let's say we lick our lips, and everything is sweet.

Recovery
Anika Carpenter

I'm the kind of person who'd go to bed with a man who sells books, I think. He'd thumb pages as he dreamt. The guy asleep next to me is showroom-still. The creased sheets will mark him. In the morning, he'll wear a pattern like sand after the tide's gone out.

I lie back, try to summon last night's exchanges. 'Here, here,' I beckon our dusty grey, rabbit-fur-phrases. I'm drowsy – my head's anvil-heavy, tight around my temples. I remember him stroking my hair, telling me to 'sleep it off', and I laughed. I tried to pull him on top of me, declaring, 'I'm not going grey; I was struck by lightning!'

A breaking yowl of fighting cats makes the air jagged, brittle, but I still have to shake him awake. 'Hey, hey, was I struck by lightning?'

He groans, illuminates a grimace with his phone, 'It's three a.m., and yes, Stevie, you were, as you put it, "struck by lightning". Four times now, just two more to go'. He rolls over and is motionless again. I think of that trick magicians do, whipping a tablecloth from under plates and cups, disturbing nothing. I'd like almond croissants, black coffee and pomegranates as props. The desire reminds me that my greying hair's nothing to do with electricity, and my words come out stumbling.

'We have porridge for breakfast, don't we? Because "there is nothing unsettling about cooked oats"?'

'Yep.'

'Do you own a bookshop?'

'We met in a bookshop. Go back to sleep.'

'What book did you buy?'

'I didn't. Go to sleep.'

Tom makes my porridge with milk, not water, sweetens it with a teaspoon of honey. That's something.

Rabbit Heart
Georgia Cook

I once knew a girl who kept a rabbit in a cage between her ribs. It was a real rabbit, and a real cage; thin metal spokes running from neck to pelvis in a perfect bell-jar shape, empty of everything except the rabbit. She fed it carrots from time to time.

I asked her once what it was called.

'Oh!' she spread her hands over the curve of her ribcage. The rabbit wiggled its nose. 'I've never called it anything.'

'Nothing at all?' I asked.

'Well,' she said, thoughtfully. 'Do *you* have a name for your heart?'

I said I supposed I didn't, but that most people's hearts weren't rabbits and didn't require cleaning and feeding twice a day. Nor did most people's hearts keep them awake at night, chewing on their ribcage.

'Really?' asked the girl. 'How strange. I always assumed they did and that you were just better at hiding the cage.'

She tapped my chest with her neat round fingernail.

'See? I can hear it moving around in there,' she said.

I wondered if there were more people out there with metal cages for chests, housing not just rabbits but cats and dogs and birds. I wondered what it would be like to have a fluttering starling heart, or maybe an elephant heart; something old and wise, crushed down into impossibly small confines. Or a goldfish heart, gasping and breathless in a cage it hadn't been built for. I wondered what it would be like to have nothing in one's cage at all.

I wondered what my heart would look like, if I could see it.

Fever Van
Julie Evans

The boy shoots through the door, whirling, excited.

'They've come for Jonny!'

'Who?' She looks up from kneading her dough.

'The Fever Van.'

She wipes her hands on her apron and goes out into the street. A crowd has gathered around the ambulance. As she watches, a man in a face mask carries the child out to the waiting vehicle, wrapped in a red blanket. Jonny Sykes is a cheeky little bugger with a filthy mouth on him, yet there he is, a limp bundle in the man's arms. She can just make out a flash of his dark hair. She shivers.

A fever van in the street means the start of an epidemic. Was her own lad not playing with the boy only last week? He stands beside her now, holding his nose. She crosses herself and sends a sympathetic glance across the street to Irene Sykes, who is standing there watching the black doors of the van close on the child. He will be gone for weeks. Perhaps forever.

She knows what will follow. Men will come to disinfect the family's home with chemicals that will make the children's eyes water and their lungs struggle for breath. The wallpaper will be stripped and burnt. And Mrs Sykes will watch her brood in fear, to see who will fall first, whose throat will close, whose skin will erupt.

The woman shoos her own boy indoors. There is mould on the walls and a ghost in the roof space, but it's a safer place than the street. She glances around. Behind the Sykes' house – now marked in the mind of others by a red cross – the chimney of the cotton mill belches thick smoke. The church clock chimes the hour. One o'clock. One single bell. A premature dirge, a knell half-muffled by the hidden sickness in the air. The crowd has dispersed, but at the end of the street, beyond a pair of wrestling dogs, she spies him sketching on the back of an envelope. She has seen him before. A lonely man in a trilby and a grubby overcoat. They say he collects sadness. And paints it.

Accidentals

Elizabeth Moss

I saw him every evening until I could have sculpted him from memory. Then I saw him a few times more.

We were not in love. Nor was it a case of raw desire. I am not even sure I could say I liked him. It was unavoidable. The first time he looked at me, I knew that something could happen. It was not a big step to making it so. He started to speak, and I raised my eyes to his, and he stopped, mid-word.

A woman came into the shop on a Wednesday morning. Memorable because it was the day the storm pulled the outdoor chairs from the bar opposite, and I thought the woman too small to risk being hit by one of those. She ought to have been sheltering in a burrow or sitting prim in the window of a doll's house.

I want you to stop what you're doing, she said.

Maybe she is squeamish, I thought and stopped carving the outline of a hawk into my arm.

I mean, him, she said. Stop it with him.

We tested how long we could maintain silent eye contact for. Several minutes. She won. I nodded. After she left, I finished the hawk. It took on an expression reminiscent of hers.

At night I hummed and looked at the space he had never slept in. By day I stood outside her window, willing her to look up from the grand piano. She never did. Her fingers played on, for him and for me.

The Lyrical Lie
Warren Paul Glover

The lie was so beautiful it couldn't possibly be true.

But that didn't stop her wanting to believe it.

It was ornate in its obfuscation. Elaborately elegant in its elusiveness. And brazen in all its brilliant boldness. A wonderfully woven hoodwink.

Shameful.

But it did the job. It deflected, avoided, body-swerved away from its author's responsibility which was, of course, the point. Who'd want to be found out telling a fib like that? If he'd been caught he would have been called a 'twat', and much more besides.

The rat.

But had he overplayed his hand? His castle of deceit built on sand...

When spinning a web, be careful of loose threads, for they can, in the end, lead to heartbreak and sorrow, if – like a detective – the victim can follow the trail of the prevaricator; anger brewing – slowly – percolating, until, reaching boiling point, the scales fall and woe betide the fabricator of it all. For revenge is a dish best served—

...well, we all know. And so did she.

She played along, laughing at his song of wrongs, sleights, feints and falsehoods. Knowing all-too-well that the ne'er do well would be hoist with his own petard.

And she was happy to hand him enough rope.

The dope.

The Other Mountain Is on Fire
Tom O'Brien

Our bikes lie tangled in the trembling grass. The multicoloured plastic strips that stream and dance from your handlebars when you cycle past my house are from a more childish time. Now they drape my thorn pricked saddle.

Some nights I wonder which you can hear when you glide by; my music played loud or my parents downstairs, fighting.

I point to the mountain where my father, the part-time fireman, retreats from rampant gorse fires threatening the woods. The black earth left behind makes fields of its own, growing stones in the ashes.

Above him, I search for shapes that aren't there in the curls of scented smoke drifting towards home.

When you lie back on the rough grass, I move my hand above you, my shadow moulding to the landscape of your body. Each fold and tug of cloth stands in contrast to the cool river revealed at your neck, smooth skin rising over fine bones that lead to your mouth and your eyes, brighter in my darkness, until you pluck the cloud from the sky to bring it, and me, to you.

In the ancient protection of the gorse, we hide our lips from the sun. We map each other with closed eyes until a lark calls across the valley, crying for the nest my father couldn't save, from the fire a stranger set that grew beyond control.

I pull away, disguising fear as gallantry. When I try to hide in the mottled blue, you stand, leaving the grass to shiver.

But you don't leave. You place yourself between me and the other mountain.

'We can eat these,' you say, throwing a yellow blossom down to me.

I taste the bitter almond while you slip from your top with a smoke sinuous curl. Give your back to the brazen sun, to the fire, to the town we bury our lives in, and I know; for something new to grow, something has to burn.

Toadeater
F J Morris

The hiccups had plagued Lily since her mum died. A year later, when she came to see me to do a seance, she could barely speak.

'Bring her—'CUUP—back,' she said, defiant, with one finger down on the table hanging like fishing bait. A hiccup rippled through the air. She believed her blight would disappear if she could have one last reckoning with her mother. One last chance to bury her unfinished business.

I hated my part. I had to pretend to swallow a poisonous, lumpy toad; my eyes closed as if diving into a pond, swimming between here and there. The room was teeming with forewarning.

Murky.

Sticky.

Humid.

Lily's son, a tadpole version of her, wriggled his fingers like tentacles. Lily's eyes swallowed the room as she watched me. I commanded her to wade into the ritual with a powerful memory.

'I fell into a—'CUUP—and almost—'CUUP. She wouldn't— 'CUUP—help me.' She gulped in air. Her sentences were like a mouthful of missing teeth. Her son anchored down her arm to stop her from jumping like a fish out of water.

Nobody expected her mother to *actually* show up. She never did when she was alive. So when she dropped from the ceiling like a sinking ship, her white hair afloat like reeds, Lily's voice croaked altogether. We all stagnated, our gaze pooling at the sight.

Her dead mother stared up at the ceiling as she swam without progress, bubbles racing her, escaping from her, up and up and up, trapped in an infinite torture. My ears popped as we sank deeper together, watching with bated breath, eyes bulging, to see if she'd ever break the surface. We were holding in more than air, more than toads wriggling in my pocket, and even Lily wanted to see her mother take a breath. So there was no reckoning, no words, no fight from Lily. There was not even a single, solitary hiccup.

The Wrinkling of My Glabrous Skin Is Proof That I'm Alive
Morgan Quinn

I am not fighting or fleeing. I am sitting. I am sitting in the bath, and I am staring at my fingers the way I did when I was a child, fascinated by the creases, the crinkles, the crumples that come from immersing my skin in water. This is what I will look like, I used to think. This is what I will look like when I am old and worn and weathered, when all my children are grown, and all my life is lived. My body will be a storybook, creased from too many readings.

You lived your whole life underwater. You were not wrinkled but folded like laundry.

I am sitting in the bath, and the water is swallowing me. I am a little girl again, going to the beach with Pops and wading into the sea, fearless, an open packet of crisps scrunched tight in my fist. The waves are grey, wild, hungry. They choke me down, down, down, and Pops pulls me back up, his puckered palms wrapped firmly around my wrist. He holds me safe in the steadfast grasp of his wet-wrinkled hands and tells me that I am alive, that he has hold of me, that nothing bad is going to happen to me. And I grip his neck with my own furrowed fingers, and I believe him.

My fingertips were dry and smooth as polished wood when you slipped through them, still and silent as the night. Your fingers were small, perfect; the crescent of your nails heron blue.

I am sitting in the bath, and my tongue slides between my teeth to taste the salty tang of the sea.

Peeling Vegetables
Jamie D Stacey

This is about peeling vegetables. I first learned to peel all vegetables from my parents, who said it was the right thing to do. 'Because it's clean,' they said. 'Because it looks better, because it's ungodly not to do it,' they said. I never questioned it.

I peel all my vegetables. I try to do a good job; most of the time, my incisions are perfect – nothing lost, just the outer skin removed. No one even notices. Occasionally, though, it's a botched affair; I slice off an inch or two. The worst client is beetroot – it's like it bleeds when I cut through, jagged, baby red tears smattering the worktop.

I met a girl horrified that I peel vegetables. 'It's barbaric.' Later, she talked about other things before saying she felt sorry for me, that my parents had been misinformed, selfish.

Today everyone is weighing in on the peeling vegetables debate. Tradition, religion, and even the WHO now tells me I should be peeling vegetables. People are talking about it on TV, *This Morning*, but a man says it's 'mutilation'. It's even made the German courts as '…an affront to decent human behaviour.'

This is about peeling vegetables. That's what I tell myself. I look down at my own peeled carrot. This is about peeling vegetables, except not really vegetables and not really peeling either, which is too nice a word. These days there are stories of men who come forward; in shame, embarrassment, even trauma as they open up about their peeled carrots and cucumbers and emotional scarring. It's becoming a movement, it's becoming recognised.

But it's only when we visit the surgery, and the doctor is describing the motion, the *incision*, that I look at my four-year-old son and decide he's old enough to make his own choices in life.

No Longer Defined, She Is Beyond Definition
Donna L Greenwood

In the supermarket, she merges with the crowd. She absorbs their eyes and thoughts and lungs. She breathes them in and chokes on their everyday hatreds. She melds with the kumquats and passion fruit and feels the sweated labour of their origins. Her body blends with plastic bags and bottles, and her hands become polyurethane tendrils wafting above the ready meals.

Outside, she becomes the street, flat and hard, mouthing her greys as people walk over her. She takes the weight of their tread and swallows her scream.

When she gets home, she melts into the kitchen walls. Her unseen hands cook food which her family gobbles up, but nobody reaches out to stop her disappearing into the walls again.

In bed, her husband's muscled will flattens her into the sheets until her face disappears into the pillow, and she becomes cotton crisp and folds herself away.

When she holds her hand up to the sun, the shape of it blurs, and she is no longer sure where her skin ends, and the light begins. She has forgotten her form, her lines, her boundaries. She has forgotten the shape of a woman. She doesn't fight against this vanishing of self, she embraces it. She falls inside it and allows the unravelling to begin. Her endless legs unfurl and spool downwards into the infinite earth, her arms reach up to the sky and cradle the moon, her eyes become planets orbiting the everlasting darkness above. She opens her mouth and drinks in the universe. She becomes everything and nothing, and in these final moments, she remembers her true shape and it is miraculous.

Part of Me
Charlie Swailes

You ask if I've got any kids, and I laugh lightly and say no, but one hand automatically goes to the silver stretch marks across my stomach, where I housed two growing babies, and the other reaches across my breasts, scarred and deflated from nursing them through their infancy.

You mime a melodramatic wipe of the brow. Eyes rolling and smile relaxing. Phew. Thank god!

I laugh again and swirl my drink and wonder how long I can hide my used, battered body under layers of itchy Lycra and black cotton. How many times I can fold myself into too-tight clothes and plaster myself with too much makeup, hiding the emotional baggage I store under my eyes and in furrows on my brow.

You ask what I do to relax, and I affect a casual demeanour and say this and that, and talk of restaurants and cinemas and weekends away, and I say nothing of the long weary nights of unsettled crying and working and budgeting and that screaming, mouth muffled into a pillow, is sometimes the only way to relieve the hard, heavy ache in my shoulders.

You nod and tilt your head and smile and understand nothing.

You ask how long I've been single, and I truthfully answer four years, but inwardly struggle to define myself as single when I am in fact three people who need food and shoes and crayons and touch and warm words and money for school dinners. And I flick my hair and touch my neck and point my knee and think of them waiting at home for me, crowding the bed and crowding my mind and cosy and soft and part of me.

You ask me if you can see me again, and I look to the floor and nod with mock sheepishness and know that I will not see you again because being the woman who laughs and relaxes and is effortless and carefree is almost as exhausting as being myself.

Kittens
Rachel Malik

She lived off-grid, *naturally*. He spent four nights in her garden, washing in spring water. Quite an experience. Figs and peaches for breakfast, picked from the trees. When his tent collapsed in a sudden storm, she let him sleep on the veranda, but when he needed a shit, he had to risk his arse and give it to the earth – a patch of ground seasoned with a compost of her own devising. I didn't ask him what it smelt like. I was more surprised he'd lasted it out: four nights in a tent and however many on the veranda.

For once, his account came without commentary. We'd gone out for a drink, our first since he'd got back, and after the usual small-talk, he talked at length about his strange stay. Not his usual kind of place: eight kilometres from the nearest village, off-road, no electricity. The house was covered in vines, clutches of embryo grapes and all the woodwork was peeling Eau de Nil. A huge garden with a well and an ancient chestnut tree right in the centre. The roots twisted and locked under the house. One day no doubt it would all crumble, but everything had such character. Everything.

Was he detached, or was he besotted? The details could mean either. Black coffee with fennel seeds, the homegrown diet of marrow and spinach, goat's cheese and radish. She even made her own clothes. So she wears clothes, I said, but he wouldn't stop. And I poured more wine and wondered if this was just a tale of Summer, or the prologue for a woman who would come to stay (and perhaps shit in his garden), a woman whom I would meet.

She kept a cat, he told me, tiger-striped, topaz-eyed. It brought him a dying lizard and birthed its kittens under his camp-bed on the veranda (he had never liked cats). She wouldn't think of getting the cat spayed of course – *so unnatural* – and drowned the litter in a bucket of spring water all by herself. He dug the hole, though.

Alison.

Leonardo da Vinci
Ibrahim Salihu

Tepid zephyrs. Moths fluttering. The whiteness of winter. Beyond the waste of rocky space; The boundless expanse of the Atlantic Ocean; The untold secrets and grandeur of *Pointe du Raz*. Time stops. *Finistère*.

Genesis.

Grandpa and I watch as the sun drowns helplessly in the ocean, tearing into transient bursts of flashes, sound of water.

Fiery red, stretched like grandma's full lips, shrinking, dying.

A lifebuoy's nearby, it could clutch onto it, I imagine.

Grandpa turns widdershins, then deasils as if he'd found the secrets to immortality.

'There goes the laws of physics – shattered, defied! A baptism of the sinner by the saint,' he says.

Grandma flashes her set of teeth, tea-stained, less than thirty-two, celebrates with him.

I ponder whether the sun is the sinner or latter while my eyes probe the optical phenomenon captured by grandpa's lens as an observer, a critic and a grandson.

Press forward, inside *Musée du Louvre*, Paris.

Bullet-proof glass shelters the half-length portrait of a woman like a protective mother.

Grandpa walks up-close, sees her enigmatic half-smile, turns and shoots a hostile stare at me as though I'd deliberately skipped its mention for literary minimalism.

Grandpa starts fidgeting until words explode in his mouth:

'Lisa del Gioconda!' He screams as though he named her.

Grandma laughs sadly, so thin the genome of a virus. All hell will break loose, I anticipate.

Grandpa approaches grandma, holds her hands, caresses them like Leonardo picked colour from his acrylic paints aisle. A beguilement.

He kisses her lips like Leonardo applied the thin viscous texture of oil paints on primed canvas.

He traces her sacral curve, eases downwards until his hands rest beautifully on her buttocks like Leonardo's sfumato rub over the chiaroscuro – that subtle, tonal transition between light and shadow.

Grandma smiles like the Mona Lisa. An acceptance.

Grandpa's eyes meet my own. He smiles, nudges me a knuckle as if to say that's how to forestall a tsunami once a butterfly flaps its wings.

A Welcome Break from the Apocalyptic Norm
Joanne Clague

Just the afternoon before, she had been kayaking in the bay, dipping her oar into a millpond that reflected the deepening blue sky. A seal showed its doglike head every now and again, always resurfacing closer or further away than predicted, and she imagined it whisking under the surface, dodging shower curtains of jellyfish, intent on surprising her.

This morning she had woken to find the sea in a temper, breaking its contract with the land to flow over the promenade and foam across the street, where it whispered the secrets of nature on her doorstep, then retreated, disappointed. The regional traffic report warned of trees down, roads closed. Her route to town was clear.

She checked her reflection in the rear-view mirror – eyes carefully decorated above a bare mouth – and looped her mask over her ears, ensuring it fit snugly across the bridge of her nose. She sat for a moment before switching on the engine, lulled by the drumming on the metal roof, breathing in the headache-inducing scent of lavender fabric softener.

At her desk, marooned in her carefully calculated space, she was eager to agree – Yes! It was a beautiful day yesterday. Can you believe I was kayaking in the sea? And now look!

Some bore stranded on his own island declared that changeable weather was normal for this time of year and watched his colleagues' eyes glaze over but didn't understand. She wanted to explain to him how thirsty they were for the commonplace in a drowning world.

Autumn let winter in, bowing at the door.

The Lesser Light
Aroha Te Whata

Some lights are just born to shine brighter. Even in the womb, I was the moon to my sister's sun. Ultrasound scans saw one twin take cover behind the other. My sister, a leading lady loved by the camera before she was even born, or so the story goes, or so the story went.

If her sky was awash with blue slurpee and vanilla sundae swirls, mine was like grey clouds in a drought with no rain. And if she was destined for great things, well, I was a good person.

Not that her good fortune ever stoked Iago's curse inside my heart. Truly it didn't. Truly. How can the early morning stillness hate the sunrise that eclipses it with such verve and birdsong?

I pushed an empty wheelchair away from the doorway and took a mental note to toss the flowers drying in their crystal vase. The strong scent of high-grade cleaning products pushed back against the fresh, crisp sheets and peppermint lollies.

They were the same lollies my grandmother used to give my sister and me when we were children, and now she insisted on bringing them to the hospital by the bagful. In the wake of a tragedy, everyone does what they can, no matter how irrational, be it lollies no one needs or flowers whose slow demise we're now forced to witness.

I wiped the spittle that dribbled down my sister's chin. She was delicate and withdrawn. The dullness of her glazed-over stare gave no indication she knew how far she had fallen or that she was lucky to be alive. *Lucky.*

The mortar and pestle of catastrophe had ground her iridescent wings into a fine powder, and I was the mediocre impression of all she had once been.

How You Should and How You Will
Elizabeth Moss

The baby cradled in my right elbow stares at its feet. One wears a white sock. The other wriggles, liberated. Its body is too warm. I can't tell which of us is transmitting the damp feeling to the other. I reach behind my ear for the cigarette I store there.

You must be fucking kidding, George says.

I abandon the idea and address the baby, saying something like, don't you have lovely toes, because questions to the unspeaking always begin with don't you and aren't you. Don't you look gorgeous? Aren't you a wonderful creature?

George is striding over. Since becoming a mother, she strides.

You can't hold your niece for five minutes.

George's intonation suggests a question. I have no reply. The baby had been handed to me on arrival in the way a glass of wine used to be.

I want George still to be a person.

A series of terrifying choking noises emanate from the thing in my arm. George tickles its tummy and says, aren't you chatty today? She looks up at me and catches my unarranged face. Something breaks. My sister recognises a lack. In the gap that is supposed to hold joy and love, I have only a suspicion that I will one day drop the baby while walking downstairs.

I visit each week. I make the noises I should. I ask about sleep and feeding in the correct language. George knows the truth. Some days she forgives me by putting the baby in its bouncing chair rather than passing it to me. The chair increasingly strains under the weight of the fat being. Some days she takes the cigarette from behind my ear before I have said hello and splits it in half. Who's to say she doesn't pick up the pieces later, hold them to her philtrum and breathe in heaven.

A View from a Bus
John Wineyard

The cold outside is causing the warmth from the packed bodies inside to condense into lemon droplets that trickle to the rubber ledge. My head is cold and intermittent pangs of nerve pain remind me I should ring the dentist. A man with an under-chin beard sits opposite. His trolley blocking the path for prams and wheelchairs. He doesn't mind. Sitting on the aisle seat shopping bag on the window one, people standing all around. He's not bothered.

In my head, I'm screaming, 'Move your fucking shopping, you selfish cunt.'

I wipe the stream of cold condensate with the back of my hand, doesn't make any difference, still no view. I know what's there anyway, an endless façade of grey, unloved shop fronts. Dirty pavements and illegally parked cars making navigation difficult. A street cleaner is shouting, waving his hands, indiscriminately. He frightens two Asian girls; they move away quickly. The look in their eyes says, 'He's not right him.'

I stand up, turn around three times and touch my left earlobe with my right hand and sit back down.

The seat is clean.

The bus is warm.

The man opposite is reading *Huis-clos* and is seemingly enjoying the irony. He nods a polite acknowledgement whilst occasionally glancing out of the clear window at a sherbet sky.

The streets are tree lined, and independent shops and cafes are filled with cheerful well-dressed clientele. I have a feeling of contentment. The knot of anger and resentment in the pit of my stomach has gone. Serenity prevails. A whistling man pushing a council waste bin is trying in vain to find litter to pick up.

My teeth have stopped aching, and all my hair has grown back.

The sign outside says Welcome to Guildford.

Motherhood Is a Series of Mistakes
Sarah Klenbort

Beginning with the birth plan, which doesn't go as planned. Baby comes two months early. Your fault: you were carrying her. Was it the glass and a half of wine on your birthday? Laps you swam in that unheated pool? The PhD you insisted on finishing? You never did yoga once during pregnancy.

Then you drop the baby. She seems fine, landed on a rug. But who drops babies? Alcoholic dads in Irish memoirs. You wean too early – or too late, depending on the book – which is bad for baby's brain, affects her IQ, which will never be as high as it could've been if you'd fed her organic fruits and vegetables.

Potty-training: a disaster. One accident after another – wet undies, wet socks, urine dripping onto shop floor. 'Terribly sorry,' you mutter, rushing out the door of David Jones.

First day of school. Now this you prepare for: make a book filled with pictures of the walk, the teacher, the hook to hang your bag. You have her practice wearing the uniform. But no one told you how you'd cry when you said goodbye – big ungainly sobs on the train on the way to work remembering all the mistakes you'd made

Just the start!

Homework: you don't make her do. And even though she reads all the time, not in the right way. The teacher explains this as you sit on a child's chair, overlapping the sides. Mrs Mason gives you a look that says, *of all people, surely you should know how to read?* But your daughter doesn't want to predict what happens next in the story.

Neither do you.

Puberty, you're not expecting. Surely this beautiful child will skip that awkward stage. The teenage years you bumble through, remembering how haggard your own mother looked when you were that age. You ask too many questions or not the right ones. You don't let her get Snapchat or Insta, the apps you need to succeed as a teenager.

And then she's grown and gone. Fucking up on her own, on a grand scale now, all because of you, her shrink tells her. It all goes back to the mother.

Rubble of Longing
Dettra Rose

A Jamaican nurse stops you entering the ward.

'I think he's gone,' she says.

He's still warm. *Daily Mirror* and flat cap on the chair. The machines are silent. You hold his wrist.

A smiley Filipino nurse swishes back the lilac curtain. 'Breakfast?' You shake your head.

'Sorry!' She tugs up her face mask.

The funeral director is swan-like. Elegant, pale, distant. You listen to her practised empathy, her suggestions. Manage your tears, lapping. Tie them up tightly in waterbombs.

Later, you turn your father's door key. Smell him as you go in. Don't open the windows to let him out. Slide down the hallway wall and stroke the worn blue carpet. Sit there till your legs go numb.

You pull the battered stainless teapot from the sink and boil the red whistling kettle. Press your fingerprints on his dust. Break into his oak writing bureau with a kitchen knife. Rifle through photos, stamps, receipts, documents...

Examine the faces and broken cabins of your ancestors. Haunted looks and happiness are handed-down stories. Recall tales of both told in your father's Geordie voice. Hug a velvet cushion...

Read love letters from the ladies in his life, Pamela and June! Fill the room with question marks. Fling out his cupboards. Linen, blankets, shirts. Undo his sock balls. Drink his precious Jameson's.

You curl up on the butter-coloured rug. Feel his footprints. The ghostly ones. The silent ones that made no imprint, or so you thought. Let grief capsize you twice. Once for a father. Once for a stranger.

Dawn arrives on your face in cold peach shades. You find coffee and Coffee-Mate.

Google: How to write a eulogy? Read: 'Traditional eulogy for Dad.' Laugh like you're crying. You write down.

'My father. Alan Dean Fox. Al. Foxy. Dad.

In his twenties, Dad was at Wembley cheering for England.

In his thirties, he became a master carpenter.

Last month, age seventy-eight, he bought Nike trainers to play table tennis.'

You feel the five-minute chasm the eulogy must fill. Count on your fingertips the years you didn't speak. Ask the rubble of your longing if another past was ever possible.

The Things You Grew
T L Ransome

You came in early, jacket-over-shoulder, glasses out of sight, pot more ponderous than seven years ago. You raked the starched white ballroom and settled in the row behind me.

Good morning. I turned and you smiled, and I swear you were going to hit on me without remembering, so I smirked and watched you take the hint, start digging through your mental harem to find me.

I was there to find.

I was there on your first day when you showed us the hard curls of Clodion, Bartolini and Canova. You stood florid against their pall, knowing full well that you were man and they were marble.

I was there when your advising periods got overbooked with girls who'd gone to Homecoming because you'd chaperoned, girls who'd worn their first tulle and taffeta for you, girls who needed a father, a brother, a therapist, a seer, a god.

Now, among the coffee cups and conference sessions, we made a date. I'd call you, and we'd go for a walk. Then back to my room so you could see how I'd grown up.

When I called, you begged off. *Tired,* you said. *Tomorrow?*

Tired? You? *Nah. I'm busy.*

Six months later, I was wondering why you hadn't told me. *It was peaceful,* they said. Your pot had been growing tumors for a year.

On shoe-points lapped with winter salt, we filed by your shrine: sketches, photos, scrawls in yearbooks. All your women, wearing black.

Afterwards, I found a bench by the ice-chased lake. I thought fondly of the things you'd done, and the things you hadn't done, and the difference between them.

Delivery
Kathryn Clark

It wasn't that he left. It wasn't even the manner of his leaving. It was what he left behind. Black sock fluff on pale carpet. Speckles of stubble that peppered the sink. A curl of silver hair on his pillow. And the dust that coated everything, made from his skin. She'd turn the bedside light on and get the sudden scent of him.

Online, she found what was needed. Added it to her basket. Clicked next day delivery.

That night she dreamed he was beside her again, a solid lump of gristle in the bed, his snores rattling her bones until she fell apart.

The doorbell woke her.

She restacked her skeleton, wove her muscles back together, smoothed out her skin.

On the doorstep, she found one parcel. Delivery.

She pulled apart the cardboard that smelled of vomit, the unnecessary plastic wrapping, the tape that left sticky traces on what was inside.

She dusted, swept and vacuumed his particles until he was collated, and placed him in the brand-new urn.

When evening came, she unlocked the cupboard under the stairs, breathed in the scent of quiet dark pasts, and put him on the shelf with the others.

She Loves You
Leonie Rowland

She has made you sandwiches with egg in them – the least attractive kind of sandwich. You hate sandwiches, and since everyone is getting ill these days, they could feasibly kill you. But you say thanks, take a bite, and realise that you would rather sacrifice your life than offend this woman.

She loves you not.

Late at night, the crack of light under the bathroom door is enough to make you notice her.

Which one of you is watching?

You need to pee, but you turn over because adjusting to the light would mean admitting there is darkness.

She loves you.

It is a question of proximity. You could move to another city and be free of her, or you could stay here and bind your bodies with Sellotape.

This is what we chose.

You could feel her press against you, allow her to become you.

She loves you not.

You might leave this room and enter another, and when you open the curtain, it might look like sunlight. But you will grow old in clothes she chose for you, in a room she decorated, in skin she touched.

She loves you.

She has made you sandwiches with egg in them – a frequent kind of sandwich. You blame yourself for not telling her, but you know she has noticed you pale when they touch your lips. She binds them with cellophane, watches you unwrap them.

This is what you chose.

More than once, the layer is so thick you are sure there is nothing beneath.

She loves you. She loves you.

Hell Is Alarming
K J Ruga

Everyone gets their own room uniquely designed to the set of circumstances that have brought them here. Brad Woodshaw's walls are filled from floor to ceiling with alarm clocks. Buzzing, beeping, ticking. All at different intervals. This was his punishment for using the earsplitting 'wonk wonk wonk' alarm clock soundbite in his student film.

The clocks that click torment his mind. The ones with only numbers beam so bright they burn his eyes. He resets one, only for it to go off again as soon as he walks away. Tiny men in lederhosen have never been so intimidating. Bursting from behind closed doors, wooden pipes dangling from their mouths, accompanied by an endless symphony of cuckoos. Brad's right eye twitched as he helplessly strangled the little man back in his woodland home. He now understands the meaning of the word 'cuckoo'.

Cords drape in every direction, chunks of metal litter his floor. They all continue to count time without electricity or weights. He abhors the particular FM-receiver that blares 'Walking on Sunshine' every day as it turns 4 p.m.; although, he is fairly certain 4 p.m. comes eight times a day in this place.

There is a bed in the corner, decorated with an exotic Lisa Frank cheetah print of neon lime and pink that makes him wish he was blind. A clock above his pillow squirts water at the top of every hour. The mattress has been soaked through for years.

The devil once smiled and told Brad he could sleep when he aligned all the clocks to the same time. He lied.

The Silent Sacrifices of Mothers
Katie Piper

Photographs of Anita's belly cover the fridge door – striae, mottling, the dark line from her umbilicus – a burnished passage from tree to bud. My temples flicker – will I love my baby, as if he had grown inside of me, will I feel like a real mother, a real woman? I gnaw on pulled loops from my cardigan, and the chill from the stone floor aches my thigh bones.

I go to bed in my tatty pyjamas, I side-sleep, empty belly breathing into a bundled blanket, his flailing limbs detailed in the dark-room beneath my lids. Gusts hurl ruptured magnolias at the window – the tap, tap, tap wakes me – they surge above the vacant cot, some have come too early, and the icy wind shivers their tawny down.

Have you known the ruins of an early spring-glimpse – winter returns to seize the miss-timed hatchings of catkins inside their warm sweaters.

Tickets, planes, hotels, births – choreography failed. Rows of plastic cots, tiny feet boxing, blankets wriggling, purple cries – pleading, alarmed – there is no oxytocin – only plodding feet, caustic perfume, and disinfectant.

The silent sacrifices of motherhood – I could not afford the 'best chance' package, so I took a 'standard chance', and the wind-raging jealously that tore around my womb when Anita sounded flouncy, or easy, and seeing him curled on Anita's chest, her waxy-bloody entrails clotting around his eyes, mouth, nose.

Snatches of him in a hotel room. The nurse, a different one from yesterday, holds him up to the screen with her fat arms. I press hot spots of breath, my voice a scrambling, quiet siren – searching for love, because I know the cord between giving him everything, and nothing, how easy it would be to turn my closed fists to the sky – stretch that cord, and then break it, forever.

Soon, I return to my blanket. Anita to her own hungry children. The nurse to her quiet house.

And my baby searches for his mother, because he is part of her body. The body he doesn't yet know.

The Complex Art of Matriarchal Duplicity
Kathy Hoyle

When we were young, my mother amused herself by pitting my sister and me against each other. She would whisper a lie to each of us, then watch, like Commodus, as we fought.

My mother taught me how to loop soft wool around a crochet hook, doubling and tripling stitches to make baby shawls. I wrapped my newborn daughter in the last one she ever made. Her lemon scent lingered as I held them both close.

One Christmas, we cowered behind the sofa as my mother screamed obscenities at my father. She threw her favourite blown-glass vase at him. It bounced off his chest, spun across the kitchen tiles but never shattered. By Boxing Day, it was back on the windowsill, sitting stoically between a desolate angel and a narrow-eyed reindeer. For seventeen Christmases, it mocked her lack of strength. She never filled it with flowers.

My mother once drove two hundred miles to my university armed with Jack Daniels and painkillers. She sang lullabies to me all night, while I writhed in agony with a whisky-soaked tooth abscess. The next morning, she held my trembling hand as the dentist worked. When she drove home, she took the Jack with her.

We were instructed *never* to answer the phone. So, with the first ring, my sister and I would sprint like hounds to pick up first, elbowing each other out of the way to slide bare legged down the bannister. I was faster, always first to whip up the receiver and smirk when I heard the disappointed click of my mother's lover putting down the phone.

My mother refused to pick out the splinters from the back of our thighs.

My mother read with me every night, tracing her finger under the words, gently correcting when I stumbled. On my first day of school, my teacher wrote 'knowledge' on the blackboard and asked the class if anyone could read the word out loud. I was the only child to raise my hand.

My mother told my sister that I was her favourite child. My mother told me that my sister was her favourite child.

My mother lied to us both.

Beguiled by a Wild Thing
Danielle Baldock

The Japanese have a word: MoshiMoshi.

It will save you from being beguiled by a fox that has taken the shape of a person. MoshiMoshi, you must say, as you speak on the phone. If your beloved is secretly a Fox, they will not answer; in this way, they are revealed. MoshiMoshi, and if the one you long for, down the long and arcing phone-line, longs for you too, they will reply, MoshiMoshi, and your heart, held still and silent, will beat again. Your feet will tap, your breath will flutter in your chest. MoshiMoshi, they will say, and you will know they love you too.

But perhaps you wait, a chill creeping through your blood, ears tuned to the smallest sounds. Yet, they do not speak. Icicles run spiky in your veins. I can't hear you, you say, breathless. Did you say MoshiMoshi? The air vibrates in silence.

You hear them breathe, but they do not answer. The phone goes quiet; the static lonely silence oozes into you.

At last, chilled, you know your beloved is a wild thing. Sharp claws have rent your heart, and you will not be the same again.

MoshiMoshi, you whisper, echoes bouncing from the corners.

MoshiMoshi, and you know you are alone.

The Lovers' Bucket List
Laura Besley

Last night we wrote a bucket list. You put 'See the Northern Lights' on it and 'Go on a cruise to the Bahamas'. I said I wanted to visit all the places my mother had lived as a child, but I couldn't remember where she had been between Nigeria and Dubai.

But, really, there's only one thing I want to add: Fall in love again. To feel that rush. That heady, giddy silliness. You can only feel like that when you're falling in love.

Remember when we were first in love? We used to prepare extravagant meals for each other, drink cheap red wine, stay up late, sharing the minutiae of our lives until, lost in each other's bodies, we'd finally drift off to sleep.

It's not that I don't love you anymore, far from it, but could I have a holiday from our marriage? I could live on Kos for three months and have a summer romance. Or rent a cottage in Llandudno and have a winter tryst.

'Morning, love,' you say, and pull me towards you. 'Sleep well?'

'I was awake for a bit,' I say. 'Thinking about our bucket list.'

'Oh yes? Got anything else to put on it?'

Being with someone else would never work because I wouldn't be able to tell you about it, and you're my best friend; I've told you everything for the last thirty years. 'Oman,' I say. 'That's the place I couldn't remember last night.'

This Is About the Starfish
Sam Payne

Blue has chained herself to Paignton Pier. Right by the entrance next to the cash machines and a mechanical ride-on horse with an out of order sign around its neck. She's protesting against the trade in starfish. They're harvested from the ocean, left to dry in the sun, destined to become keyrings or trapped behind the glass of picture frames. Fourteen and she's sensitive about things like this.

A small crowd has gathered by the time I arrive. A police officer talks into his radio. A kid on a bike rides around an elderly couple eating warm doughnuts from a brown paper bag. The gulls squawk overhead, and a bruised sky threatens to break.

She's used her father's bike chain. The one he left behind. It's looped around her wrist and threaded through the paint chipped iron railings.

'How does this help them?' I ask, lowering myself next to her.

'I'm raising awareness.'

When Blue was a baby, her father left her on a bus, and she rode it alone for six stops before he even realised. Joan, his mother, said it was normal, lots of new parents do it.

'Blue, this won't bring him back.'

She digs her heels against the wooden boards, 'It's not about him. This is about the starfish.'

She doesn't know about the bus, but there have been plenty of times since then when he's left us. If you asked Joan, she'd say it's in his nature, he doesn't like to be tied down.

'Do I need to get the bolt cutters?' The police officer asks.

I know starfish are strong, and when they cling to a rock, they are saved from being hurled around in a storm, and I know Blue's right; this is about the starfish. I tell the police officer no, that won't be necessary, and I ask Blue for the key. I undo the chain, but only enough to wrap it around my own wrist. Only enough to connect us both to the railings. And the two of us sit there, tethered to each other, tethered to something larger than us, something solid, something completely unmovable.

When the Wheels Stop
Christine Collinson

With a pencil, she carefully winds the wheel until the loose tape tightens. She loads the cassette and presses 'play'. Synth-pop booms through the clothes-strewn bedroom; into every fibre of her.

The same Pet Shop Boys track has been lodged in the chart since late summer. She begins to sing. Her hair-sprayed fringe doesn't budge as she tilts her head in front of the mirror to apply mascara. Blue like a Mediterranean sky. Two coats, endeavouring to keep the wand steady.

Her thoughts drift to Joe. The way their hands brushed accidentally in a simultaneous reach for the volume control. Her stomach froths like cola. She longs for him to be at the Friday discos, but sometimes he fails her heart.

She tries alternate earrings, clipping and unclipping, assessing the effect. Settles on neon yellow zig-zags, a near match to her socks and the belt of her ruffled skirt.

A final blast of toxic hairspray. Her frosted pink lips shimmer back at her. The song's cascading to a close; the pulsing drum-machine falls, rises, falls. She feels ready, if he's going to be there; *especially* if he's there.

The cassette clicks to a halt, and 'play' pings up. 'You'll wear that tape out!' he'd said, laughing, the last time they'd listened together with friends. He'd tried not to smile because his braces were new.

But in diminishing light on the outskirts of town, another wheel makes its final turn. The colossal pit-wheel grinds to a halt; another coal seam will fall redundant after decades of yield.

Joe's father is a miner. He'd said he wants to follow his dad, looks up to him in many ways. Joe had teased that the girl he marries will need to be content as a pit-wife. She'd cuffed him on the arm but had to turn away as her cheeks flushed.

As she grabs her jacket, the jaunty six o'clock news theme's audible from the lounge. The powder-blue denim feels reassuring on her bare arms. 'Bye, Mum!' As she clicks the front door closed, the newsreader's voice fades, and the promise of her future draws her away.

Oblations
Jane Copland

I don't fear God.

The car won't move, engine in full song, its death knell chiming against the bonnet.

'God fucking *damn* it.' Dad's hands slamming on the wheel in rhythm with his divine invocation, a mile from school. '*Jesus fucking Christ.*'

I fear being wrong, being imperfect, being dirty, being ungainly. I fear the weight of the heavy blazer pulling my shoulders into my collar bones with a bone-grinding ache, fingertips brushing the velveteen lining. I fear the sweat matting my dress shirt to my underarms, soaking my tights, squelching in my blunt lace-ups as blisters burgeon, and I fear the headmistress's office where her strangely fanned fringe and tapered bob shake as she shakes her head at me. I missed chapel.

'It was an important service for your peers,' she says. Not for you, mind, heathen.

Her blazer fits, as tailored as the humiliation. A deity in business formal. But her fingers are gnarled, torn at the cuticles with red scabs at the corner of each thumb, telling of the hours during which she'd sat at the desk and let anxiety win, whittling her own skin down to stinging raw dermis. I stare at the hands, and with haste, she hides them in a prim clasp behind her back.

'Our car broke down,' I say.

'Whose job is it to be here on time?'

'Mine.'

Lipstick creases and cracks and shows the gummy grey underneath like milky hot chocolate. It's the price she pays for a smile that stretches too wide, the price of a mouth that rolls its vowels around too many colonial plums, of lips that purse when she hears me speak, and the others: the girls whose families' cars break down and whose accents make her wince and who don't take Communion. I don't fear God because while He noted my father's request and made His way up the hill to damn the car (and what a magnificent job He did of it too, the engine destroyed beyond repair and steaming hotter than the deepest pits of Hell), I had already set off in the other direction, afraid only of His representatives.

A Minimal Supersymmetric Standard Model of the Universe
Alan Michael Parker

It's physics: everything's a string. I know because I went to the hardware store, up and down the aisles and aisles of twine, and fishing line, and cord, and hemp. Polypropylene, nylon, sisal. Twist ties, zip ties. Cotton thread and silk thread on the shelves in Crafts. Measuring tapes and two different kinds of rope swings, one with coils and the other slipknots; one with a bench seat, the other a loop.

So I went outside: contrails. So I closed my eyes: rivers, wakes, and riptides.

I knew you were angry, and what could I do.

If I could see the invisible, then the invisible could be something. Conversations like ribbons, and sentences without regrets, and feelings like buried power lines, and what I was feeling at breakfast with you following me all day, like the slow trail of memories of a slug on the brick walk.

I have tied a string around my pinky finger, to remember. People get married with strings around their wrists for luck. I would make the mind a polyhedron, to remember.

Later, there will be aisles and aisles of stars, phantasmagorical strings of party lights, impossible streamers across the sky.

I will come back to you, because you are on the other end of the string.

A Shepherd's Care
E A Colquitt

The eating drew her, the calm workings of their mouths on the grass. One dozed off, right in the middle of the field; the others ate around its woolly outline. Not a care in the world.

She brought three – one wether, two ewes – back to her wary village: 'But nobody wants meat anymore!'

She shrugged. 'They've passed their methane tests.'

They still do. Each tail has an embedded scanner, sending on-the-hour readings to computers that take averages. She's never had a red flag.

Every morning, she walks the ewes, now, to the sea, the tarmac lanes merging with dust-cloud paths. Across the bay, the Priory dominates the headland – far enough from the cliff to be safe, but too exposed to avoid the climate. They get everything up there, and went green to make use of it. When the committee chose solar for the southern roof, the vicar insisted on arranging the panels himself, in the sign of the cross.

Today, they wink at her in the sunlight, all in a row, an empty Calvary. Figures flit around below – more than usual for a Monday – but there's no wooden box, no white gown...

She can't think what's happened. It's not like the vicar still has his car.

The old tracks are rusting from the rising ocean onslaught. Seaweed always tangles around the metal; she makes sure the ewes are grazing before she explores. She likes to salvage whatever the tide leaves, but last year she lost the wether to an unexpected jellyfish.

She's more careful now. There's a dark, soft mound in the grass, which she creeps towards. It forms into an empty wine bottle, nestled in a bundle of vestments.

She glances behind, to check that the ewes are still busy; they don't need to see something like this. But they've followed her anyway, nibbling at the grass. Not a care in the world.

Luckily, when she inspects closer, the man is snoring. By the time she gets him awake and standing, the ewes are finished, waiting. She weaves his fingers with the docile wool, then steers her flock inland, towards the Priory.

People Present on Carnaby Street
on a Saturday Afternoon in Early May
Matt Kendrick

Four murderers, one of them with horn-rimmed glasses. A steady flow of pushchair mothers who divert to left or right around the woman handing out homemade fliers. Boys who fold the proffered fliers into paper aeroplanes – one of which the flier lady's husband catches and crushes. Fancy dress girls off to McDonald's for twelfth birthday celebrations, dragging despondent fathers in their wake. The dad who knows twelve is nothing compared to thirteen, fourteen, fifteen. Sixteen Pixie Lott lookalikes spaced out through the afternoon, each drawing the eye of the other pedestrians because they could conceivably be someone who the fancy dress girls should be chasing for an autograph. An off-duty policewoman without the necessary energy to be civil to the flier lady who has three years' practice scanning faces and recognises her from the missing person case long since put on ice. The local journalist who wrote an article on the case in which he described the girl – blonde hair, green eyes, like that pop star – and cast aspersions about smilies and stars. A psychic with a message from the dead which the flier lady won't hear because her Lucy is still out there somewhere and someone must have seen her. A mime sprayed in white, the colour of acid – other times, he does pizza deliveries, pulling pints, rushed transactions behind Bonmarché. The reverend who used to visit the flier lady's house on Tuesday mornings to offer spiritual guidance and cadge a custard cream. A former neighbour who nods at the flier lady then at her husband sitting nearby polishing his horn-rimmed glasses. A homeless man staring at the pedestrians' scuffed trainers and kitten heels, remembering the mismatched converse of a blonde-haired busker and how she always gifted him a fiver from her takings. A woman with hoop earrings not called Lucy who twists away from the flier lady's urgent grasp. An artist painting a watercolour sketch of the scene in which the only people present are a man selling rainbows and a girl with a tangerine guitar.

Hereditary
Hollie Richards

My mother stopped dusting in 1993. She said however many times she wiped the dust away it would only come back. She always knew when I had moved something because I could never quite return it to the clean spot on its dusty plinth.

Soon she stopped washing her hair. She said the definition of insanity was repeating the same actions and expecting a different outcome. That her hair would always get dirty again whether she washed it or not. It fell in lank strands of wet pondweed around her jaw. Our house took on the musty smell of attics and barns, and my school friends stopped coming around for tea.

I watched the shoots of madness branch through my mother's fingers. I watched the bud enclose her mind, bloom black and violet in the shades of her self-inflicted bruises. When I saw her fade, leaves yellowing and pale, I hunkered down and waited for the Spring. But the permafrost set hard, and I looked on as she withered. Absent, until she was just the parts that get left behind.

Now, I watch the swell of my belly move with life. I wonder how far the seeds have fallen. Whether the wind swept them clear or if they are embedded in my bones, waiting to grow.

Peacock Shimmer-Blue, Lips So Pink a Shocker
Nicola Godlieb

From a prick black pinpoint edge, browns gold out. Whites widen to lashes, to peacock smudge, two-tone shimmer-blue. A wink.

We look good.

'Looks really good.' You smile.

Next lips done so pink, a shocker, so dense it's a pact. We dot our cheekbones too, zigzag, swirl, sherbet bright, a bite.

Where now.

'Yeah. Where shall we go?' You grin.

Dart the ginnel since Maz on the corner might see, and then Shell will know, and then that's bound to get back to Dad.

So we draw our anoraks softly, and dizzy up into the fields, run our strident beauty amok round trees, turnstiles, kissing gates. Dash willow trails, splash the gully. Roll the hill down, round like dazzley, prized, painted eggs.

Someone there.

'Who's them standing there?' You say

A boy small, eyes wide tight. And a shadow in the tree has him caught. Him tugging, like a little kite. Untangle him, kick the shadow 'til it's pieces and lift him, run the hill. His feet dancing the puffball grass seeds.

What happened.

'What were you doing up there?' You say. And he cries.

When we get back into the town, his smudgy face asks what are you, are you angels or aliens? We shine our zigzags, all righteous fiery.

Later, Dad does find out from Maz, and we get the belt.

Eyes close.

Is that the way.

'Isn't it the other way round though?' You say.

In the woods behind the estate and shouldn't be. Eyes caught on a figure, his face slant, just standing. Holding an animal limp to his stomach, mangy, no face or legs, or anything. Offers us it.

Run home so fast, flying. Run to your room. Dad says boys don't sit at dressing tables. But there I find you, peacock shimmer-blue, lips so pink a shocker. You, angel, alien. My shimmer-eye. No one touches us.

Good for Her

D Brody Lipton

WINTER 2020 FIRST PLACE

Dad tells Mom to feed the damn cat. She obeys but appears hollow. She pads to the garage, gets in the car, and drives away.

Postcards arrive addressed only to me. Dad never reads them, complaining instead to his buddies that he wishes she'd made dinner before going. On a map at school, I trace her movements.

In Ludlow, she works at a Coke bottling plant, stationed beside a broad-faced woman from Ecuador who hasn't seen her daughter in twelve years. 'The *drogas*.'

Mom ices cakes at a Pittsfield bakery until the owner burns it down. She sells the car.

There's a mad painter she lives with in Albany, cleaning his house while he pores over canvases in his barn. He licks his paintbrushes instead of washing them.

Years pass. Dad speaks of Mom like he's spitting on the floor. When I look for my hate, I can't find it.

In a Schenectady hotel, Mom befriends a woman in the room next door. That woman is killed by her boyfriend. Mom stays in town to answer the cops' questions.

She waits tables in a Manchester diner. A grown man orders apple pie 'all aboard'.

When postcards stop coming, Dad says she's probably dead. I imagine Mom camped in the woods north of Burlington, studying with clear eyes the Canadian border, her hair a crown of greying braids.

I'm eating cereal when Mom comes home.

'Where's the cat?' she asks.

I say she ran away.

Mom says, 'Good for her.'

Handover Notes
Victoria Richards
WINTER 2020 SECOND PLACE

A morning bath is his favourite part of the day, a blast of opera, his tuneless voice; but he doesn't care, except when his brother points it out, when his cheeks flush red but he doesn't say anything, just rubs his hands together like cymbals; still, sing he does, and did, to our daughter when she was born, stayed up until 3 a.m. on the hospital ward with her feet in his hands, crooning arias from *Carmen*; placed her in the Moses basket on that first night home, all wrapped up like a small, salty parcel of fish and chips, and we didn't know what we were doing, and we held each other as tightly as we held our breaths; bought her a tiny dress she wore just once, then suddenly she was grown; taught her kindness, taught me kindness, too, kindness even in the face of *I'm sorry* and *I can't do this anymore*; so be kind to him, please, be kind; especially in December, when he misses his mother so badly that he'll wear that old black hoody with the tattered sleeves and bitten zip for days, and won't come to bed, and he'll play *La Bohème*, her favourite, loud enough for it to thump through the floor like toothache; he'll eat rice and gravy when he's sad, I know it's weird but hear him out: swollen bowls of soft, white rice, because it's hard to chew when your heart is breaking, it's even harder to swallow; and if he needs you to hold him he won't say it but he'll hover in a doorway and say nothing, over and over, but nothing really means everything, nothing means love, so love him, please; love him and if there's anything else you want to know I'll tell you.

I Was Never in The Fall
Mark Colbourne
WINTER 2020 THIRD PLACE

My milkman was in The Fall. He played on *Hex Enduction Hour*. If you catch him on a quiet morning, he'll reminisce about recording 'Hip Priest'. The postman was also in The Fall, around the time of *Cerebral Caustic*. The guy who runs the local shop was in The Fall. The crossing lady at the primary school was in The Fall. Everyone in the pub was in The Fall.

I was never in The Fall.

Most of my colleagues in the office were on *Live at the Witch Trials*. The pizza delivery man was in the touring band for *Bend Sinister*. The gang who lurk around the park were involved in some of the Peel Sessions. The girl on the supermarket checkout co-wrote 'Kurious Oranj'. Everywhere I go, all I ever hear is people talking about their time in The Fall.

And I was never in The Fall.

In 1998, Mark E Smith boasted that The Fall would be The Fall even if it was just him singing and your granny on bongos. My grandmother was, of course, in The Fall. She played the bongos. Before she died, she would tell a delightful anecdote about meeting Iggy Pop in New York. I wish I'd gone to New York. I wish I'd met Iggy Pop.

But I was never in The Fall.

My wife finds me crying in our bedroom. I'm sat on the edge of the bed, my head in my hands.

'What's wrong?' she asks, kneeling down before me.

I wipe a tear from my eye. 'I was never in The Fall,' I sob.

My wife smiles. The smile is patient, indulgent; it is the way she would smile at our children when they were younger. 'Of *course* you were in The Fall,' she says, stroking my sides. 'You've just forgotten, you big silly. All of us were in The Fall.'

I sigh and prop my chin on her shoulder. On the opposite wall is a framed picture of my wife with Brix Smith. They are grinning with their arms wrapped around each other, triumphant after a show in Berlin.

Phytoremediation
Morgan Quinn
WINTER 2020 FOURTH PLACE

The nuclear reactor is in meltdown again. She tries to soothe it with calming words, tranquil music, a cool drink of water. The truth is, she regrets ever becoming involved with such a volatile edifice. At night, when the reactor shuts down, she scrolls through advice from more experienced owners. Leave, they insist. You're in danger if you stay. Radioactive fallout is no joke. She chews her lip and casts furtive, fearful glances towards its bulk as she reads.

~

It's 3 a.m., and she is watching a documentary about Fukushima. They know about nuclear disasters in Fukushima. The camera pans out to show rolling fields of sunflowers and a sanguine monk in orange robes. She rewinds. Watches again to drink in the scene. Pauses to trace subtitles across the screen with her finger.

~

Phyto means plant but sounds like fight. She is encouraged by this.

Her weapon of choice is a small trowel. She creeps outside, and the earth is damp from rain. When she shakes it, the packet sounds like a summer storm. An inky teardrop, the seed sits on her palm, and she weighs its potential, pushes it into the soil with a ragged fingernail.

Already an experienced horticulturalist, an iris blooms across her cheek.

~

Re – If at first you don't succeed, try, try again.

Her weapon of choice is a spade. Its heft feels good in her hands.

One sunflower was never going to be enough.

She digs deep into the ground, shifting piles of earth until her hands are blistered. She hurls dirt at control rods and buries the pressure release valve. She submerges cooling towers in soil and entombs generators. Takes handfuls of seeds and scatters them indiscriminately.

When she is finished, the sun is a spreading stain on the horizon, and she stands in the shadow of a towering mountain of mud.

~

Mederi – Time does not heal all wounds.

She takes a Geiger counter to the spot where the reactor once stood. It clicks in her pocket, needle fluttering like a trapped bird. In the corner, a lone sunflower grows in irradiated soil, face turned to the sun, fierce as a lion.

Avalanches and Angels
Jim Toal

When it comes, she realises it's been there all this time, accumulating under her ribs, a precarious shelf of snow. Over sixteen years, a carapace of ice enamelling each layer. Flanks cresting the fathomless air, anticipating, willing its own inevitable fall.

He was with friends outside Antoine's barbershop when it happened. A masked boy on a bike, skidding to a halt. A quick jab as commonplace and innocuous as a handshake. Remounting casually before speeding away.

Quaking, sliding.

Life spilt.

White-out.

At the station, a fresh-faced policeman, a white boy young enough to be her own, shows her the weapon labelled and sealed in a plastic bag. It makes her imagine the kitchen knife she uses at home to prepare vegetables plunged into her snowballed heart.

Later, a girl-child mortician shows her to the chapel of rest. A crisp sheet glowing in the dim room. She wants to uncover the wound, run a fingertip over its ragged edges, kiss its bruised mouth.

When she was little, she had a doll that longed to be real. Plastic turned flesh, glass into living eyes, warm skin under her loving touch. Wiry whorls of hair grown long and plaited. How she yearns for the opposite now. A bloodless, synthetic body, the lustre of a manufactured stare.

The girl, stiff with sympathy, never looks at her. A trained aversion to life in the face of death. On leaving, it's the girl's false baby-doll lashes freighting her eyelids she remembers most.

That night, it snows. Through into morning. Day after day. Nonstop for weeks. The streets buffered and frozen silent. In the never dark, she goes to the spot on the pavement outside Antoine's.

Among blue-pooled drifts, she remembers him playing in the snow for the first time. From the tower block balcony, watching him scissor arms and legs to make a snow angel. With a muffled thud, she falls backwards onto the cushioned pavement. Snowflakes descend from the hidden sky to crust her eyebrows. She begins thrashing her limbs, more frantically till she rises through the rigid air. Leaving her earthbound shadow on a bed of white to fly through a blizzard of lights.

Shavasana
Alison Woodhouse

My son has returned from his dawn run and is now doing naked yoga in the garden. Before I can say what about the neighbours, he asks if I'd like to join him; says it's my last chance.

I drop my pyjama bottoms, peel off my T-shirt. My belly looks like cookie dough, and I cover my cock and balls. The damp grass is shocking.

'Fuck!'

'It's the corpse pose,' he says. 'Just relax.'

The lawn is littered with stones and bits of bark. I think of crawly things, deep underground things, but Jimmy said to relax so I copy his breathing.

Slow in, longer out.

I don't know how to do it. Jimmy's eyes are closed, his arm by his sides, palms up, fingers and thumb lightly curled. When he was seven, not long after his mum died, we went to the fairground and got stuck at the top of the Big Wheel. I thought he'd be scared, but he swung his little legs, looking up at the big old sky, then he drew circles on my palm, round and round, while we waited. Now, without opening his eyes, he takes my hand, gives it a squeeze.

He's leaving today, backpacking through Asia, and he doesn't know when he'll be back. His mum liked Devon. Cream teas, fuchsia hedges, cows. She didn't fancy travelling any further, so we never did, and after she'd gone, I didn't have the appetite.

Slow in, longer out.

Jimmy and I stay that way, just breathing, until I forget about the neighbours, don't feel the sharp stones or the bite of deep underground things, and I want to be like that forever, but he starts to move, and I come back to myself and remember what I am, a cold and foolish old man.

'You done?' he asks.

He pulls me up. I don't know how to let go, so I start shaking his hand like we've just met.

'You going to write?' I say.

He nods. We both nod, standing naked out there on the lawn, at the top of the wheel, waiting for the stomach flip, dip, drop, down the other side.

Ask Me About the Flames
Alex Reece Abbott

For Orla

She's excited about the hotel's advertised cosy, romantic fire.

Don't mention: architectural one-upmanship or the privilege and damage I associate with lavish Gothic Big Houses.

Note to self: It's only Tinder.

The ornate staircase is carved within an inch of its life, grain eyes boring out. Fat, curved handrails worn dark. Commanding newel posts, turned balustrading. Candlelight sparks a fussy crystal chandelier over eleven polished treads.

Don't say: I've seen balusters snapped into kindling.

Mid-July and still I shiver.

Obsessed with burning, we watched bleak monochrome news, mesmerised by the giving and the taking away. Down Under, fierce God was playing Enola Gay with eucalypts, raging bushfires leaving Hiroshiman devastation.

Stashed out of our reach, we discovered the kitchen matches. Loving their fairy-tale scale, like Scouts we balled-up *Belfast Telegraph* pages and set fires, waving smoky trails, believing our signals meant something.

Fighting over rasping, plastic Bics grabbed from the gutter. Yearning for sleek Zippo lighters, seductively shiny gangster accessories... that confident click. Loving the dangerous tang of flammable butane in the mornings.

Dreaming of beautiful, sapphire-edged flames, our nightmares were My Lai burning to the ground. Wearing masks of stoicism, we ran, hiding and seeking in charred car skeletons. Finding and losing playmates, as families in our street were burned-out with a match-strike. Swept from homeowners to homeless, their balusters recycled in July. Midsummer madness to be tholed.

Mid-July bringing unimaginable high-rise-one-upmanship. Our house water-doused, windows boarded-up, our streets studded with tyre-stuffed *Jenga* pallet towers. Neighbours torching our summer tarry and toxic with pungent, blazing bonfires. Smoke curling from our basement window.

Beside the corbelled Victorian fireplace, she counts limestone-trapped fossils.

Polish off that fat wedge of vanilla cheesecake.

Ask about her summers in Brittany when she was a kid.

Maybe It's Too Late Now
Jamie D Stacey

You discard a plastic bottle on the street. You tell yourself *you dropped it/ it fell/ you were late, and you don't normally do this*. You don't use the bags at the supermarket anymore. You try to avoid it in the wrapping unless it's *necessary/ useful/ convenient*. But it's everywhere. It's in the fabric of your best dress and the lining of your worst underwear. It's in the things you carry, hold, throw away and forget. It's in your entertainment, your conversations, the roof on your house. It's in your rubbish. It's in the landfills. *Underground/ gone/ forgotten*. Someone else's problem. Someone else's responsibility. You recycle, mostly. Still, it's in *the sea/ on the shore/ in the cries of mermaids*. In the guts and hearts of fish. It's on the trawlers. It's in the supermarkets. It's on your plate. It's in the silver of your knife and fork, and as you tear into skin and muscle, you tell yourself nothing. You know nothing. See no evil, and all that. It's in your mouth, in your bowels, in your toilet. Back in the sewers, the landfills, the sea. Back in the fish, on your plate, on your tongue. It's in your blood, pumping through your heart. Pumping *in utero*. It's in the foetus, in the birth, in the surgeons' gloves, in your apron, in the cries of your newborn. The newborn that *wriggles/ cries/ calls the angels to come back*.

You melt as you hold onto this bundle of joy, only to notice it everywhere; in the quilts, in the nappies, in the bottles. You wonder what you've done, what your generation has left for the next. You whisper into the baby's ear and ask for forgiveness, then tell yourself her generation might *be better/ less indifferent/ more honest, at least*.

Why I *Still* Don't Care for Jazz
Lucy Goldring

Intro

In the thick-curtained dark, our parents head-bob to boogly bass. Fuelled on flat coke and salty crisps, us kids race sticky laps of the club. Hours pass. When we call boredom, our beer-glazed adults suggest dull games, wave us off through Silk Cut smoke. We roll our eyes, and Sunday stretches on in endless improvisation.

First Chorus

After Mum reveals her affair, Dad barrels out the house, trailing blue notes –
never   the   back
*   come   fuck*
I don't know who's leaving, but I stress his banged door with fist-slammed piano notes. As discord fades away, Steely Dan's noodly groove blares from Dad's stereo – smugly claiming the moment.

Middle Chorus

Even though I'm grieving for grunge – even though it sounds like *hell* – my attendance is assured.

The festival climaxes with a mesmeric Roy Ayers, his call-and-response demanding collusion. My boyfriend claps and sings, elbows me. I brim with embarrassment, overflow with first love.

For him, *I jazz—*
and he dumps me anyway.

Overblown Solo

Childhood expires in the last place still serving. The cider is warm and sickly-sweet. On stage, saxophones screech blue murder as I un-peel my sole from the flypaper floor.

Perhaps I'm just jealous. All that unfettered delight; those blissful adlibs. *Everyone* has their life mapped out but me.

'Shittest twenty-first *ever*,' I whine tunelessly, honking on (and on) till everyone leaves.

Last Chorus (a flashback)

My relationship with Hannah was always askew. It began with a shared birthday cake before descending into spite. We're no longer friends when her jazz musician dad passes away.

The newspaper mentions a hosepipe, exhaust fumes – not an aneurism, like Hannah thinks. I picture him slumped over his clarinet and think about kindness.

I lay the paper on her lap.

Outro

Here's the sheet music: job, husband, mortgage, child. Both players know the score, but the piece unravels anyway. Under duress, I adlib bad jazz; wild and dissonant, deaf to the beat of my grief.

Afterwards, I seek out calming refrains; melodies that linger and endure. Nothing resonates. Months pass.

When the music returns, it's a punk rock anthem. I dance like no one's watching and claim it as my own.

A Grape Is a Kind of Berry
Jasmine Sawers

Our final night in the old apartment, dust still in my hair, I settle beside my lover in the dark. There is so much work to do tomorrow.

'Do you ever wish we were stupider?' I ask.

'What? No.' A laugh in the dark becomes more than sound. A laugh in the dark settles over the body like a beloved ghost.

'I don't mean like, a dumbass,' I say. 'I mean like, gorillas are really smart, but they get to just hang out in nature, having orgasms and eating berries. No cleaning, no packing, no worries.'

'I think we *are* gorillas,' my lover says.

'We're great apes,' I say. 'Which they also are. You can tell by the lack of tail.'

'I'm a grape,' my lover says.

The skin of a grape is ragged at the stem. You can peel it off for the sweet, silly ball of fruit inside, but if you don't get the angle of extraction right, the first layer is ripped away while the bitter rind remains.

The skin around my fingernails tears just the same: tender pink insides throbbing at the sudden exposure. You can put it in your mouth or wrap a band-aid around it, but still it sings its little hurt. Still your heartbeat takes up residence in your fingertips. Still the pain is bigger than it should be, bigger than narrow stripes of torn epidermis seem capable of creating. Every nerve its own unknowable universe.

I could unhinge my jaw and invite my lover to step inside, bitter skin and all. I could become the swallower of worlds. The eater of fruit salad.

What Murders Me?
Shanel Chalmers

My shoulders circle in the wind like a leaf poorly skimming the water – waiting to sink. I hold the railing, take another puff of menthol, and blow the smoke out through my nose. I savour the gritty burn birthing a cough in the back of my throat. The familiar scent of giving in. He'll smell it on my skin in the morning.

'Ahh!' I screw up my nose and drop the filter.

I head inside, not bothering to rinse the bubbling red of my finger; it's something to concentrate on at least. I grab my coffee and try to write, I sip and stare at the blank document, tobacco clinging to my everywhere. Enough mint to make a cat high if only things were different. The clock ticks by frantically.

'Another cigarette,' I whisper, ignoring the smaller voice that tells me I'm supposed to be cutting down.

I raid the kids' snack draw before rolling. The pit of my stomach aches emptily. I wipe the powdered cheese from my mouth, a Lady Macbeth paranoia, but they'll never know of the carnality that goes on when they're in bed. I proceed to roll, finger burning against paper, until it's red too.

'I'm not satisfied,' an echo of tears goes unnoticed because nights are meant for mothers.

The Fighting Temeraire
Caroline Gonda

This is the card I chose for you: Turner's *The Fighting Temeraire*, one of your favourite paintings in the National Gallery. The last time we went there, when you were still well enough to come up to London, we sat in the room for a long time looking at it. An old warship being towed for scrap, a steam-tug puffing merrily away in the foreground and the sun blazing on the right.

A hero ship at Trafalgar, then a hulk storing provisions, then a heap of parts to be sold. Five thousand oaks went into the building of her, and how much iron to fasten the wood? Not valueless, but no longer treasured. Except that Turner makes a treasure out of this last voyage, this imagined ending.

The National Gallery was always our favourite place to go, full of the things you loved. Dutch flower paintings and interiors, Turner, Constable. An egg sandwich and a St Clements fizzy drink in the café, your treat. You'd talk to the gallery attendants, ask them who their favourite painter was. *This is my daughter*, you'd tell them, in each room we went into, as if you could never get tired of saying it.

The florist looked surprised when I gave her the card. Most people go for florals. Or something religious; it's a church funeral, after all. It doesn't matter. Nothing matters now, except to say goodbye to you in a way that's about the two of us, a way that feels true.

Disinsection
Chris Milner

There are mosquitos in here somewhere. The other passengers, still noisily boarding, usher them in with their carry-ons. They hide on coattails, cling to overnight bags. Tonight, they will sleep with us, seek adventure, feed richly, live life to the full, find love and fulfilment and probably die before morning. They will, no doubt, catch us unconscious, violate us, drink our blood, deposit their gifts, perhaps leave us their babies – and all before our turbulent descent onto the plains of Uttar Pradesh.

Tomorrow, we will only discover their marks as we're buffeted along the expressway to Agra, while we plough through the madness of the Delhi *yaataayaat* – cows wearily ignoring us, families clutching each other on scooters, motor horns serenading as we weave in and out, dwarfed by bright-painted trucks. We will gouge the imprints they left on us as, at last, we race through the serene gardens, pass the long ponds and the manicured shrubberies – scratching and scratching at the itching welts as we remove our sandals and skip hot-foot across sun-scorched white marble and into the mausoleum. Their worst will only emerge later, once our return to the city has begun, the fever taking hold of us on the back seat of the taxi.

They are closing the doors. We are trapped. I can hear their triumphal droning. They smell me. They come for me. But, no. There is gas hissing from canisters held high all along the aisle. Hold your breath. Does it work? Has it got them all? We listen, catch the faint whining of insect death. Or, perhaps, the foreshadowing of tomorrow's suffering.

Sonata
Rayna Haralambieva

Pastoral   *appassionato*

Bach's Partita for Violin Solo No.1. The notes burst into existence –
delicate and boundless. The audience breaks into applause. It's close
to ecstasy, close to something out of this world. She's only seventeen.
'A virtuoso,' people whisper, eyes widened, mouths half-open. She
wins awards, bursaries, hearts.

Lamento   *ritardando*

'Abductor pollicis longus, extensor carpi radialis longus, flexor dig-
itorum profundus.' A small part of the muscles that make the
movement of the human hand possible. 'Any others?' the professor
says. She can't remember. Her thoughts have slipped into Paganini
and Bruch, and Sibelius, and how the heart lifts with each movement
of the hand. She'll have to study harder, she thinks and holds her
breath.

'Extensor carpi radialis brevis. It extends and abducts the wrist.'
'Excellent,' the professor says.
The violin stands pressed against the wall in her room – a pun-
ished child.

Oratorio   *lacrimoso*

At her graduation she plays Elgar's Salut d'Amour. She gets some
notes wrong, she's sure. The piece breathes and moves and speaks,
but to her, the notes are heavy and lost – a fallen bird.

Requiem   *maestoso*

The hall's full, and all eyes are on her. 'It's the left ventricle that's
the largest and strongest chamber of the heart,' she says. She's made
a name for herself – a well-respected cardiac surgeon and a clinical
teaching fellow. Students wish they were in her shoes. She wishes
she could go back to where they are.

The talk comes to an end. She looks at people – their hearts full
and strong, and true like music. Her eyes catch the light of the dying

sun fighting its way through the window. She smiles. The hall bursts into applause.

A brilliant talk by a brilliant mind. A talk on the human heart and its resilience.

A Man Walked into a Bar
Susan Wigmore

Or rather, you walked into the café where I was eating beans on toast. But I wanted to try out that line for old times' sake, and boy, it felt good in my head. I knew it was you from the off. You pointed at the menu, and the guy behind the counter poured a coffee, no milk. No offence. You took the cork stopper from your mouth and drank.

I'd seen you perform next door at the comedy club, way back, before it was boarded up and activists sprayed it with tags and slogans and called it democratic art. I remember laughing so much my stomach hurt like I'd been punched. You were so good, man: Carol Vorderman on *Countdown*? Like an autistic shelf-stacker. And those uber-woke men who offered to castrate themselves to show just how in step they were with #MeToo. Tell another one, go on. Tell another. Carpet sticky, fug of fags, that leaf-mould smell of old beer. Just one more. Faces split with laughter in the dark, a breath of fresh air. Go on. To hell with it.

You tipped the cup back and drained the dregs of your coffee that wasn't white. You looked done in, a dog with no teeth. The fat guy behind the counter noticed you'd finished and put on his marshalling face. A jobsworth we used to call them. You left then, cork stopper back where it was when you came in. No lines crossed.

There were deep bite marks in my own stopper. It would either be replaced or the silencing order lifted next time round. I flicked it across the table. It rolled to the edge and fell to the floor. I downed my black coffee and went out into the rain. To hell with the lot of it.

Kind of Blue
Conor Montague

Ghosting along damp, deserted streets in the pre-dawn gloom, cherry blossoms pale confetti beneath my feet. Mute trumpet keens from an open second-floor window. *Flamenco Sketches*. A slender woman silhouettes in soft backlight swaying to Coltrane's tenor saxophone. I stop. Sip of her solitude. Two of us alone together. Tune washing through my veins like primo junk.

Movement ahead. A fox freezes in the act of crossing. Leaves rustle castanets above our heads. Neither of us should be here, yet here we are, skirting the shadows of this toxic city, demonised by the tortured multitudes who will monitor through locked down panes from daybreak. We will be out of sight by then. Curled deep into forgotten crevices. Away from the hostile glance. The accusatory glare.

But for now, I will dance slow upon drenched petals. Breathe deep of the rain-rinsed breeze. Dream my way to The Church at that moment when the stars aligned and those cats surrendered to the notes and chords and beats, and broke free. Free to lose their selves in the collective. Free to find the collective in their selves. Free to distil the pungent mash of the past into one pure present.

One take. Those cats nailed it in one take.

Stubborn, It Continues to Grow
Nicola Godlieb

We throw her hair to the sky. It cluds dully-soft over deck chairs, sprays into tilted refrigerators and up the hessian of a torn lampshade. Red curls from cream manilla, an envelope marked *E' 89*, brought here to the tip and upturned.

We can't keep everything, love, you say, lugging over a suitcase of door handles.

And she couldn't take it with her.

Descended part-Viking our family, both raiders and hoarders.

There's a tale she liked to tell, of an exhumation. Rosy-tea tresses brimming a coffin, oxidised to gold, and a poet's manuscript retrieved, worm-holed. Like love, hair doesn't know when it's dead and stubborn, it continues to grow. Spreads itself across generations.

I catch a blow of her copper, watch sunlight bounce a sunset.

Your gran had it too, a talk-of-the-town gold-red. Titians, they'd call us, after the painter. And colour disinters itself, up through frames of black and white.

My own is pitch as night.

A raven breaking its own wings, you blazed, when once I'd lopped it off, the bathroom floor clumped like mowed grass. My cropped head an inky full stop, marked me out from the start, the black of difference and dark as forgetting. You wrapped the cuttings in newspaper, kept safe by your bed like a pet.

We swing her last box, her biro'd *TV Times* and frostings for diabetic carrot cake. As you drive us home, the boot bouncy-light, I want to snip a tail of your hair, white as lit titanium.

Lost Symphonies
Iona Winter

The bus glides over bitumen highways, and I think of spindrift strung together on stems, like saliva. Beside the road, on land scraped back to clay, ancient trees once stood. Does the earth remember lost symphonies of sound within her deep valleys?

A child behind me is asking a million questions while their feet punch a code on my seat. What's that? What's that? What's that? When I glance back, the mother withdraws the offending boots.

Undeterred, the child drags their nose down the glass pig-nose-style, hands spread wide, each fingernail glazed a different colour – resplendent.

~

Before I left you, I dreamt of a place where all the rivers converged. Everyone we knew, or are yet to know, was there. The water held our histories and our futures – infinite possibilities. Waterfalls, ancestor pools, and surging rapids lay deep in the reflective skies.

My heart attuned to a warbler's song, and when I felt the earth's pain, my legs trembled. The quiver of my chin matched the ancestors, regardless of my skin tone. And my shaking hands told me all there was to know about who I am. 'This is the place of your people,' they crooned.

I saw how every event was a precursor for another. Day turned to night, light sieved the trees, and the moon emerged pale on the horizon. Like the stars hanging low, I knew my place. Then it became so cold spiders took to crafting their webs close to the ground, but the earth still held warmth between my bare feet and her skin.

~

I'm returning to a city filled with earthquake-rubble-mounds, where bedraggled orange flags flap in the breeze. In transient marketplaces, mad men will pound out their sonatas on tin whistles. And high above them, a woman's spray-painted face remains watchful over the stones.

It makes me laugh how we have treated our mother like shit for eons, and nowadays can't stop complaining because she's finally retaliating. I always knew violating her would have consequences.

Some damage is irreparable – like the breath of a furious wind upon fragile saplings, or splinters beneath my nails marking out dark channels.

After a Double Shift at Asda Where the Customers Were Savage About the Lack of Toilet Rolls

Sam Payne

Nineteen months since the fight at the football match, and now you're telling me there's an abandoned city in our closet.

This isn't fucking Narnia, I want to scream, but your consultant is in my head reminding me of the unpredictability of brain injuries. *Your husband may experience memory loss, hallucinations and strange behaviour.*

You limp to the bedroom, and I watch you kneel down and peer through the wooden slats.

'Alright then, what does it look like?'

We used to play this game when we were teenagers, but instead of abandoned cities, we would imagine our future – the jobs we'd have, what our children would look like.

It takes so long for you to find the words I butt in because I want to order Domino's and watch back to back episodes of *Breaking Bad*. I look through the slats at old coats and football scarves and describe derelict buildings with sagging roofs, crumbling walls and shattered glass.

'It's desolate. Everything's ruined. Do you want pepperoni or margherita?'

You slump back against the bed and stare at your no-good hand, and the sad, slack look on your face knocks all of the rage out of me.

Sliding down next to you, I say it won't always be this way. Soon, the wilderness will take over the city, and the animals will come. There'll be deer grazing in the mall, monkeys swinging from street signs and elephants all in a line trampling through Boots self-service tills. You laugh, so I keep talking, and eventually the slow rhythm of your breathing tells me you're sleeping.

I must be drifting too because the room fills with the smell of forests in autumn rain. Our bodies shrink to the size of conkers, and yours works as it should again. We walk hand in hand through the gap in the closet door, through the wild city and for miles along the railway line. When we find ourselves at the mouth of a train tunnel, we stare down the darkness and sing football songs, loud and out of tune, until our voices croak and our throats grow tender and raw.

Bloodshot Body
T L Parry-Sands

We only went downtown for coffee and new-to-us records at Dr. Disc. Downtown was dying. Almost every second shop was shuttered. Instead, closer to home, we ordered deep-fried, spicy squid at Ly Hoa Tran after I closed the theatre and cleaned the popcorn machine, after you pressed your nose to the glass door, waiting. We used to be able to eat that late, following the closing credits of some obscure arthouse film at the little storefront repertory cinema, as soon as I ushered the audience out and the projectionist locked up his booth and went to wherever projectionists go after work. We used to imagine that he'd gone to watch a film he didn't have to thread and show himself.

You loved pineapple chicken in a half-shell at one-thirty in the morning because the waiter spun it on a giant lazy Susan from the opposite side of a table meant for more diners. I complained my writing assignment was boring. *Seeing,* I whined. *Pass that sauce. What kind of a prompt is that? Do the opposite,* you said. Rebellion hadn't occurred to me as much as following convention rarely occurred to you. *Blind,* we smiled. The squid was perfect tender. You spun it back to me.

I recognize your chin in the photo, George, and the way your lips curl in when you press your mouth closed, a stiff line, as if your life depended on never showing your teeth. It was the same for all of your photos – school portraits posed steering a ship's wheel, party photos, camping photos. And now, caught by the lobby-cam, CCTV-style surveillance – *have you seen this man?* Coffee-stained eyes, wine-stained cheeks, scabs picked clean away from raw puncture-red, wax skin. Beautiful rot, bloodshot body.

A Memory Is a Living Thing
Rose Rae

We were watching TV when it happened. It must have been the movement of his hips that gave birth to them, or the leering smile on his cartoon face. Sketchy and two dimensional, he reached out of the screen to shove them inside of me. Three maggots. Sharpened pink fingers inching and twisting beneath my skin.

The kids shrugged and rolled their eyes.

'Why'd ya have to be such a drama queen, Mum?'

The pads of their fingers stroked the lime-lit screens in their palms.

'S'life, innit? Not everything is about you, y'know.'

They stuck around, those memory maggots. I took a wrong turn on the way home from the supermarket, watching helplessly as they explored the length of my body, licking at me from the inside. I drove blind for a full ten minutes before the purple-bruised heathland pulled my gaze outwards again. When I made it home, the ice-cream tub wept fat tears of solidarity.

I hated them. One, bloated and bile coated, tore at my stomach. Another circled my eyes like the kiss of an onion. The third squatted behind my fingernails. Living grime.

When you look at me now, do you see me or my maggots? They are still there, twisted into my flesh. But they're only a few millimetres long, after all. The rest of me is so much bigger. When they whisper to me now, I hear the squirm of fear beneath the poison of their words. I am learning that kindness to insects breeds kindness to myself.

Once, I had a dream that they pupated and flew out of my body, iridescent in bottle-green and sapphire. In the static hum, I watched them leave. I ran my tongue cautiously over the empty spaces inside of me, oddly bereft.

Target
Eliot Bryter

I grew up thinking that being in a room alone meant I had to be ready to run. I would shout out for someone, but the house was too big, they didn't hear. Up to me to make a run for it, slamming the doors before my Entity followed. Sometimes, I'd go far, down the village road outside in snow.

My mother would sometimes appear sudden in that house too, slam the door behind her, tears leaving her face like they were getting away before the cold entered.

I dream often of the unfinished bathrooms years later, the kitchen extension my dad and Ray Moth built, but memories are through my Entity's eyes. Me playing with a doll's tea set. Me banging a spoon on a bowl in my sister's pram.

I'm at a scraggy café in Portugal, decompressing from the Casa das Histórias Paula Rego, a cake of a building with pink walls, a seafront town. I'm dizzy with the heft of Rego's painting, *Target*, energy hitting me like flies on a screen. It depicts a woman kneeling on a cushion, facing a heavy black curtain that is drawn closed, but with movement, as if He paces, judging. Her dress is unzipped. Her wide feet are bare, thick with dirt. She pulls her dress aside, chest naked. Go on then, she says to someone out of view. Here's the target. Do it!

Or else, she is alone in the room, practicing for later.

Or else, talking to her Entity as he walks inside.

A tree cuts my view of the harbour in half so perfectly it's mathematical. When things get hyperreal, impossibly perfect, the cold enters.

I pick up a brochure from the table. Luxury apartments, 700 Euros/month. Rustles in my ear when I turn the page, glossy paper tutting. Entity eyes flit at my back. Older, fatter. President of the Ex-Pats. A photo of Ray Moth.

Him touching my ballet tutu. White, with sequins. Oil from black, dirty fingers.

My mother spreads my legs in the bath; red trickles to pink. We can't say anything, she says. Dad started a business with him only last week.

There Must Always Be Another Way
Lucy Hooft

She pinned her heart to a paper parasol. Where the pin made its incision, the paper bled, spreading through capillary threads until the parasol beat with her blood.

It was eye-catching, her blood-red paper parasol. Soon everybody wanted one. People asked where she got it from. She replied it came from me. How much to buy your paper parasol? It's not for sale; it came from me. But she liked to show it off. She was happy that people wanted it. She liked to make people happy.

Some people were jealous – why should she have such a thing? They mocked its fragility. They flapped at her heart-stained paper with their laser-printed nylon, luring her to take it out in the rain.

She didn't mind their attacks. It only made her stronger. She knew she could do more.

She worked at night, staying in, closing herself off from anything that would distract her from her work. She worked with red from her heart, green from their jealousy, yellow from the sun's last rays falling through the window and blue from the veins that tracked her arm. She grew weak after the first few had bled out, but still she refused to stop. So determined was she to make the best she could make, each one more vibrant than the last.

They found her in the morning, just a bloodless fold of skin, a puddle of bones licked dry. Her ceiling strewn with paper parasols.

You Think You Don't Like Capers
Rebecca Field

...but the truth is you never tried them, not until the tapas dinner party at your friend Raquel's house, the one where you brought the Patatas Bravas in your mother's oven dish which you forgot to take back home and never saw again, where Angie brought a salad and her older brother Zach who you'd never met before, who has a moustache which he waxes like he thinks he's a total hipster, and Raquel's boyfriend Owen brought a bag of Doritos and a six-pack of beer which he drinks by himself and you wonder why he gets away with making zero effort when you spent all that time parboiling potatoes and chopping chillies and now you can't even touch your eyes let alone itch anything down there without wishing you hadn't and you think that men with moustaches have never been your thing but by this time you've had several tequilas whilst you wait for the food to come out and Zach is looking pretty hot from where you're sitting and you can tell he's looking at you too, over the salt-encrusted rim of his shot glass, and then finally Raquel serves up her baked halloumi dish with capers in the sauce, and by this time you are starving and you load up your plate and don't even think about the capers until you bite down on one and notice and it's only then you realise that capers are great, they add a juicy saltiness all of their own, and you wonder what else you might like that you never tried before.

Pluck
Frances Dalton

When my mother was in the nursing home, I used to pluck the tough old lady hairs on her face. I liked doing it. There was something useful and cosmetic about it. As with many ritualistic and repetitive tasks, I found myself thinking of the same thing as I plucked. My husband's marriage proposal. He took me to a very swish restaurant – white linen tablecloths and napkins, a waiter in a monkey suit – and he didn't hold with that kind of show normally, so I knew something was imminent. And after the main course, he leaned over, took my hand, and said – Chris? – and I knew he was plucking up his courage, and I said, yes... My husband is not good at serious moments, and I was about to prompt him, when he dropped my hand and burst out laughing. This was hearty laughing, roar out-loud laughter. He got so giddy he literally couldn't stop. The other diners were all watching, and I wanted him to get back to the serious moment.

What is it, I asked sharply, what's so funny?

I was going to... and then he exploded all over again – and then I saw this huge hair sprouting over your lip, and I just couldn't...

I put my finger to my mouth, and I could feel it – a single hair, so long it coiled. How could I have missed it?

Anyway, he said, when the paroxysm had subsided, you know what I was going to say.

And I did, so he never asked again.

Bruises
Catherine Ogston

You swear you can feel the flesh of your arm bruise as your mother leans her weight on you. The church is only a short walk, but the pavements are white with frost and slick where puddles have frozen. In the park, there is the swish of metal blades, cutting and slicing on the frozen pond – a lone ice-skater doing tilty turns and figures of eight.

Inside the church, your mother removes her hat, displacing her wig. She tugs at it, mumbling about the miseries of hair loss and cancer treatment. She was always a talker, even at a funeral with its undiluted sense of occasion. You have often wondered if your father left so the sound of her voice would stop ringing in his head.

The service starts, and your mother silences her own speech for the minister's. She listens to the summary of Maisie James' life even though she knows every event, every triumph and disaster. Afterwards, you edge out together into the winter afternoon and start the slow walk home, your mother digging her fingers into your opposite arm. You stop at the pond so she can catch her breath, the ice-skater gliding in a curved circuit across the glassy oval.

'I stole her boyfriend once,' she says, and surprise makes your mouth into a circle through which your breath plumes into a misty cloud caught by the icy air.

'She thought she was going to marry him, until she saw us kissing,' she says, and you wonder, '*Is this my father we are talking about?*'

'She slapped me, and we never spoke of it again,' continues your mother. 'Not until we ended up next to each other for chemotherapy.'

'Then what did she say?' you ask.

'She said I did her a favour.'

She leans heavily again on your tender arms, and you wonder how much time there is left to ask the unanswered questions. The ice-skater has finished now, leaving intertwining lines laced into the ice which you know will be gone by tomorrow. Your bruises may last a week or so longer.

white diamond
Jay Kelly

sometimes there is no story. and there are no consequences. there is just being almost eighteen and wanting the independence of that mythical number to be yours. there is just being told that it will not be yours, that there are *no further treatment alternatives*, that this life, your *life, your* life, may end *at any moment*. there is just leaving the house and slamming the door because your mother won't stop with her bloody crying, unrecognizably wiry and watchful and never, ever sleeping, *just in case*. there is just your brother, squinty and re-sentful, bad to the bone, whispering *why don't you just get it over with*. there is just walking with your best friend, the girl you used to fancy, who now fancies you, and laughing about that preposterous phrase *at any moment*. there is just being in her kitchen playing *trivial pursuit*, winning well, listening to *simon & garfunkel* on her white tape recorder. there is just this funny dance she does when *feelin' groovy* comes on, with her heels and then her toes together. there is just standing up and the song being long enough for you to follow her and glide across the parquet floor side by side. there is just taking advantage when your platelets are high enough to book one of the driving lessons uncle tommy got you in the early days when things still looked *promising*. there is just getting into the car with margaret, the driving instructor, to whom you would leave your heart and its catheter, if you could, and her saying, *where to today?* and no mat-ter what you say, there is just her, brown eyes, warm on the inside, laughing loudly, saying *super!* there is just the fear of telling her that it could be *at any moment*, in case she changes on you, but you do and she doesn't, just pauses so slightly, before smiling, *super, she says, let's go*. and as the city yields to open space, there is just the longest les-son yet, the cliffs over dalkey, the sea glittering white diamond, and everything together in this exact moment.

Gum Leaf Skeletoniser
Katie Oliver

The counsellor said to occupy myself with activities that were un-likely to be triggering, which is how I come to find myself reading a book entitled *A field guide to common insects of Australia and New Zealand*.

I learn that gum leaf skeletonisers are caterpillars that moult thirteen times, but from the fourth time, they retain the heads of their dis-carded exoskeletons, stacking them on top of their current heads until a tower of hollow skulls teeters over their tiny bodies. I decide that I will do the same: when a bad thought comes, I'll just moult it out and shove the offending thing away up in my hair so it can't touch me.

The first time it happens, it's a rush, my whole body tingling as a layer peels off. I scramble to balance the delicate shell on my head, black spots bursting in front of my eyes. The flashback recedes. I feel better and moult again for good measure.

Gum leaf skeletonisers use the horns they make from parts of them-selves to bat away predators and protect their soft, exposed flesh.

A car exhaust backfires, and I almost fall into a bush. Shaking, I moult almost immediately, using both hands to steady the growing spire that makes me sway beneath its weight. Insect-small, I attempt to navigate a street that now vibrates with threat: a smashed window, heavy bootsteps. Shots fired.

Researchers have found that while gum leaf skeletonisers' horns help them to fend off an assault, they ultimately only prolong the or-deal.

I trace the pitted scar on my arm, fingertips coming away bloody with memory. I squeeze my eyes tight shut.

Gum leaf skeletonisers will always succumb to their attackers in the end.

The Difference Between My Cat
and Teenage Daughter at Weekends
Jan Kaneen

She slinks in at dawn, flowing past me lithe and lean, sliding her twi-light fur against my handknitted slipper socks. I rest my brew on the kitchen table to scratch behind her ear, which she likes just long enough to arch her head into the cup of my hand. But almost straight away, she's had enough, and springs up to the sink to catch a cat-lick sip from the dripping tap. When she's had her fill, she lollops down, eyes fixed forward, padding past me like there's nobody there, then settles onto the sofa where she curls into an immediate sleep. She's in exactly the same position when I come down from the shower, when I tidy the house, when I get home from the supermarket, but as I crash past, lugging bag after bag, finally she wakes. She yawns in slow motion, casts me a slit-eyed glance, stretches everything until her claws peep out, then shadows past me into the kitchen, skulking and hunkered like she's ready to pounce. She mewls and caterwauls whilst I fetch her food, then purrs and circles as I fork it out. Once she's eaten, I hardly exist, and she's barely aware of me as she grooms herself perfect. And when she leaves without a backward glance, all sleek and silky and twitching whiskers, I smile with pride as I watch her go, brim-full of admiration at her independent sass. I say nothing about her standoffish attitude, or lack of gratitude, or how she treats this place like a bloody hotel. I don't stand on the front doorstep barking, What did your last servant die of? – trying not to feel the gut-punch love that's been bending me double since she squawked into the world. And after she's walked past the dirt-dashed terraces under the orange bloom of a feeble streetlight and disappeared round the dark street corner, I don't turn back into the hollow hallway, muttering tearful entreaties like be careful and sen-sible and home by midnight.

Oil & Ink
Tina Hudak

Along a deserted strip of macadam plots next to the small town inter-state, there squats a 1960s one-story, brutish building of brick with grimy, plate glass windows; inside, flattened cardboard, dented cabi-nets, dirty fans, and ripped posters. Oil and grease-spills trail on the cement floor to a vanishing point. The building remains used by one car enthusiast; despite its exorbitant cost, we buy it.

The first floor is Mike's. Filled with vintage European mopeds, his tools, rags, lifts, and drawings are strewn carefully. Hand-built work tables made of heavy lumber are hefted into position. The sur-faces remain clear for not even the first day. He fills it with pieces of whatnots from the floor, the shelves, and boxes yet to be unemptied completely. 'Perhaps I could organize this for you, 'I suggest care-fully. 'NO goils allowed,' is the standard misogynist reply. I am not offended. I get boundaries.

The second floor is our minimalist, rooftop home: bathroom, kitchen, Murphy bed. Adjacent is my space, my studio. Needing little footage, I lovingly place the T square, pens and pencils, brushes and paints on a salvaged metal table repainted a deep forest green. My small pine drafting table slides between this and the low bookshelf Mike made for me years ago.

Here, light abounds, or raindrops serenade, or wind refreshes; the room opens to a flat rooftop – now a garden of sorts. Facing the back of the building, our view is one of tall oaks and maple trees with some surviving elm. Slightly damaged wicker chairs, found at curbside on garbage night, have bright new cushions and throws. Window boxes of rosemary, thyme, and oregano, some already flow-ering, tease our senses mercilessly.

Standing in the doorway, I see that his hands are relatively clean and that he has changed into a better tattered T-shirt. Yet, I can't re-sist this, my boundary, 'Take off your shoes!' He smiles. His shed. My studio. Our home. Mike grounds us with grease and oil; I dream us up with pen and ink.

Bridled
Chrissie Cuthbertson

Both loops of the browband slide onto the headstall to sit in the middle. The end of the noseband without the buckle slips through the browband alongside the headstall and buckles the other side of the cheek. The cheekpiece attaches to the headstall with a buckle at the top and to the bit with a hook stud at the bottom, one cheekpiece on each side of the headstall. The reins attach to the bit ring behind the bit.

I grasp the bridle with one hand in the middle. You are very tall and must bend your head for me to reach, and if you resist, I am deft, and I will pull your head down. You must open your mouth so that I can slip the nickel-plated iron into your mouth, and if you refuse, I am well-practiced, and I will slip my fingers into your warm mouth between your lips at the side. Though you might try to fasten your mouth against me, you are powerless, and when I touch your tongue, you must submit. You must capitulate. You will succumb.

I check that the bit is in the right place, crinkling the edges of your velvet lips. I pull the headpiece over your ears. I rest the reins on your shoulders and adjust the martingale stops. I buckle the throat lash leaving a hand's worth of space. I pass the upper noseband strap under the cheek pieces and buckle behind. I take the lower strap through the bit rings and buckle tightly under your chin.

Your mouth is a vulnerable and yielding place. If I can control your tender parts, I can control the whole of you even though you are much bigger and stronger than me. If you are still difficult to control, I can devise much harsher restraints with Kimberwick. With Pelham and shank. With gag. A standing martingale. Draw reins. Ketamine.

A curb chain (twisted).

Hypnotic Regression to a Childhood Lighthouse
Claire Carroll

I remember rain. A car park next to the sea wall. I remember the grey damp of it. The inside of a Citroen Cavalier. I still remember the ashtrays, the beige velvet interior. I remember our adult's rictus, her hands clenched at the wheel. A cruel pinching at my skin that seemed to come from inside. My brother's baby-blonde head turned towards the drab surge of the sea. A cigarettes-and-diesel smell. We walked down the slipway even though it was freezing; even though she knew we hated the jagged water.

Before they built this, the boats would smash to bits on these rocks; sailors would drown. That's why the wind sounds like screaming.

A thin causeway – ripple-ridged concrete – stretched like a pointing finger towards the lighthouse. Its eye was too high up to see us. The sea heaved with banks of yellowing foam; an animal's swollen fleece. I remember him and me, hand in hand. I remember piles of seaweed, strewn everywhere like clumps of pulled hair. We were afraid to touch it.

I dream about this place, you know. I dream of going back there and looking. I know that wouldn't do any good.

That day, though – that last day – it was smooth. Flat calm. The sky hung heavy; too hot. Our adult fell asleep in the sun. We tore away, clattering across the rocks towards a sea like a green silk scarf, jerked tight. The rising tide brimmed around the causeway; a bathtub too full. There were these shoes children wore back then, these plastic sandals. His soles were different to mine; too slippery.

We crouched together, watching ourselves in the water-mirror. Light danced on his pale body. *We could pass straight though, if we wanted to.* My swimsuit felt too tight; it snagged on the concrete as my legs slithered in. The kelp's slender limbs stroked my skin, pulling me close. I can still feel them, even now. It would be different down there. Free and weightless, we could glide away. I looked up at him, his startled face in shadow, his golden halo gleaming like treasure. I reached up and took hold of his hands.

The Portrait of a Young Woman
Vanessa Waltz

The young woman wonders what she is doing with her life.

Honestly, she sometimes swears that she can hear the crickets chirp.

The young woman studies the bakery case at a cozy coffee shop in the city. Around her are the bright peal of early morning music and the nosy aroma of coffee.

She finds certain meaning in things at this point in her unfettered life.

As to these things, money is one of them. It is a concern, wary and constant.

The young woman wonders, as her eyes flick idly over the bakery case, if she will ever be at a point where it will not be. What would that look like? (In so wondering, the young woman debates the financial merits of purchasing a roasted plum cupcake.)

Other ideas and influences call to her.

A modest career in the arts has presented itself.

The young woman has interests. She dabbles. She attends classes. Opportunities have arisen.

The young woman knows that this could conceivably be it: the exchanging of a not-so-creative-life for a creative one.

The decision lies in the balance before her.

There is always romance. (The young woman considers.)

As to men, she's not had much luck with them thus far in her fretful existence.

The young woman sips at a cup of coffee, its milky depths pooling before her eyes.

There has been a young man or two; there has been a pick of flowers offered a time or two. What's come of it all?

A few edge-of-the-doorstep kisses.

A few late nights.

To consider romance, with its swell of inelegant care – romance, or love, has found her slumped alongside the bathtub, brooding from one too many encounters.

Love is the trouble with her, the young woman concludes. She watches it walk right by.

The young woman sits here, now, in this coffee shop.

Here, the comforting coo of conversation calls to her.

Here, a splash of color is in the fashions along with a correspondent dash of dreaming.

The young woman listens to old standards in an old city at once alive and new.

The music overhead warbles on: *let there be love...*

Climate Migrants
Shanna Yetman

Thirty million migrating birds will fly over our house tonight. So leave the lights off, my dad says as he pecks my cheek. I'll stay up, like in years past, wrapped in my sleeping bag spying on birds from the sliding glass doors in our den. Dad will pack and pace – just this once, ignoring our temporary visitors. Some will land on our one-more-night back deck and nibble at our feeder. They'll call out to each other – those loons, those savannah sparrows, those winter wrens and yellow-bellied sapsuckers as they eat and sip and squawk about their trek.

These birds, I think, have all timed their move so well; they travel together. Tomorrow, we will travel alone, leaving well before sunrise, anxiety pushing us towards new problems.

You must rest, my father says to me, but I won't. I want to soak this all in; keep today in my pocket, but, already, it is almost gone.

I open the doors to hear the exotic caws of strange birds and wonder what it feels like to be with so many bodies as they move through. Does it feel like home?

We'll have a caravan of sorts too (a U-Haul and an old Toyota), but we won't maneuver in that V-shaped pattern with the wind whistling through our beings. We'll hit the highway and head north, not south, pushing away from the rising ocean waters and forever floods.

Outside, there's a blue jay. His crown is up, and his white breast faces me. He's nibbling at spilled seed underneath the feeder. This is just another migration for him. I wonder how he does it. How does he leave his home in such a hurry?

He'll be back before we ever are.

Floored
Helen Perlman

Ok. This time I will do it. I'll tell the truth. But only because it's you. You, who heard the shouts, watched the walk-outs, provided the hugs. You, who knew the truth but never judged. It wasn't you that I hid from. First, it was the shame and then the guilt.

But, you deserve to know.

I was driving.

The shimmering bitumen with its skid marks, ghosts of previous misadventures, was tempting. All I wanted was to keep driving. Away from him and the mistakes. My head was still hazy from the night before. I hadn't realised just how much I'd had until flipping Under the Pink over led me back to the kitchen to refill my glass – only to find an empty bottle. I could blame Tori and her Cornflake Girl, but really you and I both know that it had been anything but a good year.

The makeup no longer worked as a concealer. The excuses had become hollow. You'd heard them all before. They weren't all lies. More like omissions, alternative facts. But they had become the truth. At least a new version of it. The splintered spaghetti on the lino, the remnants of another failed attempt at a reconciliation revealed the truth. This had to end.

And so, I left. With my Mary Poppins carpet bag, once a source of amusement, now a sad reminder that I wasn't the 'appier bloke. For now, it was just going to be me, the road and Suzi Quatro. Past the rain beaten weatherboards, the faded BMXs, the front yard car yards. Looking for an open road, but not a new beginning. That was too exhausting to even consider.

I should have been paying more attention. Heard the squeak of wheels, seen the flash of your child's ponytail. I did feel the thud of Alice hitting my front fender. But I didn't stop. I couldn't stop. I didn't have room for any more flaws.

Late of the Pier
Nick Black

My Bonnie lies over the ocean, my Bonnie lies over the sea – absolutely huge, she is. (Rimshot. I thank you.) The tip of the pier rocks with laughter from the show, the middle's shaken by slot machines, the other end where it touches land thunders with whirl-arounds and swoop'em-ups and hear-me screams. Ropes of electric light slap the darkness into submission.

Under the boards, arse wet on brine-splashed stones, with a thermos of mulled wine. It's the end of the summer season, but there's a chill in the air this evening so... Slosh, slurp. Spiced breath waxing lyrical, 'You dis-lo-cate my jaw, Lay it gentle 'pon the floor, Love and awe, Love and aww!' and the dark serenaded sea tugs at his feet.

Fallings crumb down on his face as the wooden sky above is trod. Heavy gods. He shimmies up the beach a little, on his back, 'ksssh!' – the pebbles, slying down his length with fake shut eyes to see if the sea's following. It is, foaming at the lip. 'My love, my love!', eyes full closed now, fumiously smiling, fingers fanning, palms wet. Beyond the electrics, the blue of summer heats to purple, soaks to black.

A Pirate's Guide to Motherhood
Anne Howkins

The wind drifts her to a comma of land in an ocean she cannot name. Between the sh-sh-shushing waves, there are other sounds. Sounds almost forgotten.

She sleeps on the sand, dreaming of a girl with a rolling sea-legged gait, a girl whose first words were stolen from Blackbeard, a girl suckled on yo-ho-ho rum, a girl whose tears filled the ocean in her heart.

She drags shipwrecked timbers through the marram grass. Props battle-worn oak limbs against each other until she has the skeleton of a cabin – lashes them tight with dead men's laces. Listens to the tales the drowned seamen shush to her as she works. When she catches a cabin boy's voice, she sings him a lullaby.

She dives for kelp, bladderwrack, furbelows. Lugs her bundles to the cabin, hauls them to the roof she's boned with the stark white ribs of a pilot whale. Inhales its song, breathes it back to the ocean, a lure for a yo-ho-ho girl. Staples the seaweed thatch tight with rusted cutlasses, hands bloodied red as she works. Red as the day she birthed the yo-ho-ho girl. Red as the flag she hoists above her roof.

The waves sh-sh-shush. The voices sing of black-hearted betrayal, bodies hoisted gibbet high.

Her empty belly aches. She delves through the sea tangle for shrimp, smacking her lips as they snap, crackle and pop in her mouth. Her fingers find the soft gumminess of an octopus, which slithers around her neck, pulsating companionably to the rhythm of her heart. The creature guards her while she sleeps, sweeping sea lice away from her cold white limbs. In her dreams, she clinks jiggers of rum with her crew, drapes gold and emeralds around the perfect neck of a yo-ho-ho girl. The waves sh-sh-shush, and the drowned voices whisper.

She wakes to quiet. No sh-sh-shushing waves. No voices.

She runs to the sand startling something pale into the air, something like the petticoat of a yo-ho-ho girl. A yo-ho-ho girl crying in alarm, breaking apart, floating to the sand.

When the godwits settle, she sees bones, gold, emeralds wrapped tight in the arms of an octopus.

Beware of Toads Crossing
Julie Evans

She arrives on the dot, locking her Mercedes, striding across the car park. Orange silk blouse, black trouser suit, heels like skyrockets.

Anita is the opposite of Toad. She is Princess, morning dew on an oriental lily.

She's here, she always says, just to help me. She has certificates that say she can.

Two glasses of iced water, sprigged with mint, sit on the coffee table. I want to dive inside, sink into that vitreous lagoon, hide my ugliness amongst those leafy weeds. Drown.

Anita takes a neat sip, readjusts her tumbler to fit inside the perfect circle of the coaster. Her twin sons peer out from a photograph on the shelf behind. Their missing front teeth make me ache.

'What's on your mind?' she says.

What's always on my mind? That crouching toad, dumb and glum on its triangular road sign. *Beware of toads crossing.* There are flowers there now, turning brown, a fluttering plastic windmill and a thousand empty messages where the rain has washed away the ink. But did I swerve for no reason? Was it just a mottled stone, flattened by time, or an autumn leaf blown across the carriageway? Or did my wheels leave behind a trail of amphibian DNA, mucussing the route from carriageway to tree trunk?

'Try not to internalise it,' she says to my silence.

The twins grin their aliveness at me, each toothless space filled with Future.

'What's the week been like?' she asks.

She glances at me through a flick of eyeliner, leans forward. Why doesn't she kiss me, make me right? Can't she see that I've become my own Nemesis, flipped to the other side? Can't she see the leather of my skin, the warts on my back, the milky poisons hidden in the glands behind my eyes?

'I'm still at the toad sign,' I say.

'And still on display?'

I nod. 'And poked with sticks.'

'Who's poking you?'

'People,' I say.

But it's not people.

It's him. It's my boy.

He is poking me, flashing his copper eyes in alarm, pulling at my clothes with his spectral fingers. Screaming, 'Mummy, watch out for that toad!'

The Grand Master on Babel Pass
Louise Mangos

Once I've lost sight of you, venom churns in my gut. The road rises like a chimera. Belligerence makes my legs pump inefficiently on the pedals, pulling the handlebars from side to side, wasting energy like a recalcitrant child on the verge of a tantrum. The next curve is never-ending. I know I can't catch you. The invisible thread of your encouragement has pulled to stretching point. Until it finally snaps.

Angry words hiss from between my clenched teeth. When I run out of English curses, I use French and German ones picked up on both sides of the mountain in this tiny landlocked country. '*Chié*' and '*Gopferteckel*'. Pride rises briefly between the pain. If I can't keep up with you on the bike, at least I know all these words.

At the top of the pass, I have to vomit. A single violent expulsion onto the verge. Up comes my vitriol. Things I want to call you splatter on the ground. I look down at the masterpiece I have created. Pale orange modernist strands interspersed with pink impressionist splotches. A creamy filigree foam is applied as though with the softest of camel-hair brushes. An early Monet, perhaps.

Any sense of sporting achievement is stifled by my pounding head and sweat stinging my eyes. My chest is tight, my muscles in rictus. But this! This creation is magnificent! Worthy of a place on the polished concrete floor of the Tate Modern.

I wipe my mouth on the back of my glove, click my foot onto the pedal and push off before the acid stench bounces back at me.

As I freewheel round the bend and take a deep breath, my exhaustion is replaced by a burst of endorphins singing through my veins. I coast to where you wait, holding out your water bottle like a trophy. I take it and suck out every last lukewarm drop.

I thank you for waiting. Saccharine. I tell you that the ascent really wasn't so bad. Conciliatory.

And remark how stunning the palette of colours look on the Alp today.

Emergency Measures
Michael Loveday

The carriage doors were almost closing when he stumbled in and grabbed onto the overhead bar. He wore a full wetsuit, equipped with mask, snorkel, flippers, a bowler hat on his head and a regulation black briefcase in his right hand. As the train shunted forward, he mimed breaststroke, crawl, backstroke, swinging the case in circles with his rubber-clad arms. He clambered past us gawping in our seats and travelled the seabed in slow motion, the great flaps of his footwear slapping fatly on the floor. His eyes widened. He pointed: schools of tropical fish were flitting beyond florets of coral that bloomed in pink and green and yellow. Every couple of minutes, he would breach the surface, remove his mask with a flourish and grab at a lungburst of air. He took no heed of any of us on our way into The City. Most of us were hunched over smartphones, buried in pages of *The Metro*, listening hard to the latest news reports. Soon, I knew the carriage would be flooded and only this sensible man would survive.

Seventy-Eight Synonyms to Live By
Audrey Niven

Take away the colour, the energy, the charisma, the verve, the curiosity. Discard the crazy clothes and the hair that has been pink, blue, plum, russet, platinum, yellow, green, a mixture of them all, and purple besides. Tie it up, let it down, cut it off, let it grow. Forget about the playfulness, the boldness, the loud and the quiet. Let's not speak of the talent, the skill, the wisdom, the kindness, the fight that burns inside. Whittle away at the interests and passions, the collections, the hobbies, the created things, the ideas and inventions, until only a kernel exists. And then put that away in a box with postcards and photographs and mementoes of youth. Put aside the questing. Accept.

There are seventy-eight synonyms for ordinary.

Normal, common, customary, everyday, standard, typical, conventional, mainstream. An easy start. So-so. Liveable with. But that's only the first eight. Then comes routine, regular, fixed, traditional, prevailing, run-of-the-mill and the tipping point: boring. Are you ready for boring? Bland? Uninspiring, hackneyed, indifferent, nondescript? Will you fit in with the workaday, colourless, humdrum treadmill of an indifferent life?

You say it's only spite that makes me say this. You say it's jealousy – I always was a vicious cow.

It's just that I don't want to see you become unremarkable, my friend; undistinguished, uninspiring. By all means, settle. Decide. Make the choice.

But if we do have the choice, why not be a glorious, blazing antonym instead?

Penis Envy Yeah Right
Cathy Lennon

All night you curl around her back, foetal, feeling the hollowness of your body. In the morning bathroom, she catches your red-rimmed eyes in the mirror and spits. Maybe we should get a cat, she says. You reach to turn on the shower and lose your reply in the thunderous hiss.

Work-bound, strap-hanging, you watch a woman heave herself up as your stop approaches. She loops a shoulder bag across her bulging belly and cups it protectively as she presses past. Following behind, you echo the slow east to west of her gait. Lost in concentration for a few steps until you catch yourself in other people's frowns.

On the way to the photocopier, through the partition maze, you navigate by framed cake smashes and school-tied, gap-toothed grins. At the water fountain, you fill your eco-friendly flask while they moan about teething and parents evening. You eat your lunch on a bench, surrounded by the surging pulse of sap and budding blossom. A woman shunts a buggy past, distracted, one hand thumbing at a phone screen, and you meet the black-eyed stare of the toddler, an intergalactic connection that sends you dizzy.

That evening, you buy her favourite wine and cook her favourite meal. You talk about maybe going to Australia. Her face brightens. She's always wanted to hike in the Blue Mountains. And you say that maybe this is the year that you should. Before. She dumps the dishes in the sink and turns, hands akimbo as if to taunt you with the vacant cradle of her hips.

In the thick silence, the pill pops, and her shoulder rises against you. You lie there until her breathing slows. In the night-time bathroom you take your penis in your hand. Your emptiness stares back at you as you weep into the void.

Dolphin Spotting, Circa 2010
Martha Lane

Not allowed on the boat, I watch from the shore. Skin screaming for sunscreen. My eyes hunt, hungry. The captain said there were dolphins in there, said they were guaranteed every trip.

But Mammy dragged me away.

'Men lie.'

On a wall, brick dust collects in the creases of my knees. Churns with sweat, makes cement. Mammy pulls out a paper parcel from her dirty tote bag. Swimming in sauce, salt and vinegar. Sprinkled with batter scraps – trying to hide there's no sausage or fish. We eat to the beat of the surf on the sand.

'They're cold.'

Mammy chews slowly, shovels damp chips into her puckered mouth. I watch the lump catch in her throat.

'Seen one yet?' She nods out to sea.

I turn my hands into binoculars, search the great blanket of water. What I would do to spot the dark banana of a proper live dolphin. I try to shake the laughter of the kids on the boat; it itches the insides of my ears. They are miles out, barely a speck. Trundling towards the horizon, getting to touch the sun. The sun is cool; it's made of stars.

I drop my last chip, belly full of clay.

I stare at the ocean until my eyes sting. Seeing spots, I take Mammy's greasy hand and jump down. My toes, creeping over the end of last summer's sandals, hit something hard in the sand. I snatch the treasure before anyone sees and steals my chance to get onto that boat. The coin takes up most of my palm. On the bus, the driver had tutted at the waterfall of change jingling onto his tray, but I love the brown ones. Like chocolate.

I drag Mammy back to the pier; somehow the boat seems further away.

A fisherman pulls into the bay. Fish spill out of a trough on his deck. Sparkling, they stare blindly at me.

'Look at that,' Mammy's voice loud and high as if I should be excited.

'I like the stripy ones,' I say, pretending.

I hate their wet scaly skin. Hate their wide-open mouths and the hooks where their breath should be.

From the Edge
Lindsey Booth

From the edge, one might think the lake shallow. But the bed soon drops to deep, dark reaches. Cruel cold that would suck out one's breath. Weeds that would wrap themselves round even the most confident legs. I sit a distance from the edge on a moss-ridden bench, placed there in memory of someone who *loved this spot.*

He loved it here too.

I was never a morning person. Wasn't there when he took those shots of the lake. Instead, I hunkered down in our duvet, cocooned our warmth. Often I didn't know he'd left until he returned. Clunk of mug on bedside table. Steaming tea to wake me. A pebble he liked the shape and feel of pressed into my hand.

'If you won't come to the shore, the shore will come to you.'

Morning-chilled fingers stroking hair from my face.

I'd look at his photos through bleary eyes. Out of synch with his enthusiasm. Slow to appreciate how the spirit mist clung to the water, shrouding silhouette of courting grebes.

Dew seeps into my jeans. I roll two pebbles in the palm of my hand. Individually smooth, they each rasp against the unbearable other. The sun lips over the far shore, cradled by autumn-spent trees 'til it rips blinding ruby blades across the surface.

His mother said her mantle clock stopped the same minute it happened. That the floorboards in his childhood bedroom still creak. She senses him near her grandchildren when they play. I get no musky whiff of aftershave. Our bed doesn't dip on his side during the night. Inexplicable drafts don't brush hair from my eyes.

Ruby pales to rose gold. Solitary grebe slips under the water. I wait. Watch. You never know where he might re-surface.

Coin Toss
Danielle Baldock

When Sam flips the coin, there on the side of the road, it comes up heads. Heads means we head north, towards the river. The air throbs with moisture, heat beading our foreheads and trickling slow between our shoulder blades. Freda laughed when we asked her to come, shook her head so hard that the ribbons on her plaits blurred, settled down instead in the cool of the verandah with a lemon ice and a magazine.

Just you and me then, Buddy! says Sam, and we set off, pockets stuffed with walnuts, and the smell of the soft fallen apples thickening the air. We stop in the shade of the church as we pass, stones green with moss, golden icons shining through the pointed windows. Mrs Lewis is at the altar in her checked apron, polishing the brass candlesticks. She waves, stretches her weary back, and we step on quickly before she tries to conscript us into laying out the hymnbooks. Walking on, we get into a rhythm, and it's kind of soothing, the step, step, step, along the dusty road edge, the memories swirling like whirlpools. My mind keeps snagging on it, though: the thought of her hair when they found her, beads of water running like a string curtain as they lifted her. The blue of her lips, and the orange pigment of the rocks striping her cheeks, and her arms flopping like stocking dolls. I can tell Sam is thinking of it too, our feet slowing as we get closer. By the time we can hear the splash of the river sweeping past the bridge, we are barely moving at all. Suddenly we have stopped without quite knowing, and he's looking at me, solemn and quiet, like on the day when they laid her into the ground. He pulls out the coin again, dusts it off on the back of his pants. Best of three? he says, and I nod, fast, watch the coin tumble silver up into the air, and fall slow, slow down; the way a small girl can tumble from a high rock, and plunge, laughing, into a wild and whispering river.

Star Clock and Snowdrift
Barclay Rafferty

If there were polls for such things, the most convenient time for a power cut would be when there's snow on the ground.

iPhone at 8% charge. Fishing nets over church doors. Ghosts in white-sheet rapture. Torchlight to the snowy verge, the snow field beyond. Everything becomes rickety and ye olde, Hammer horror absurd.

No more threatening teens in rubber Frankenstein masks. Halloween, autumn, the snap of apples: gone. Just snow globes, naff tinselled ceilings, the ring-dong-ding of shuffling newlyweds. They tent in stormcoats and wellies, bundle up on couches and in beds, neon reindeer flickering on front doors decked with wreaths. Everyone loves a ritual. The Yeomen of the Guard still tiptoe the vaults of Parliament each November. I strap on cork-soled sandals on the first day of spring.

I should've chosen the sea. Been a cork soul. Lived by the star clock. Would've clanged the demons right out of me.

Keep bees in dark times, Anonymous said. They'll hum hymns in bleak December. An hour without electricity, and I'm dieting on snowballs till May; taking a magnifying glass to sleet, solving buried snow mysteries; unthawing insects from icicles. No one will steal my thunder.

Meat wagons toboggan pea-souper fog. Could cart professor or priest, pill-pusher, Jack Frost. There's no town and gown in a power cut. Everyone's threadbare, frightened of the same things: Riverdancing on black ice, divorce settlements, mistletoe requests. Will you fuck run away with her, their wives'd yell. But she's never difficult to talk to, they'd say. Her eyes burst to understand: my marking pile, ecclesiastical admin, whatever.

If you're out after midnight, someone told me, you're up to no good. Aphorisms for everything these days: beekeeping, nutritious snowball recipes.

A neighbour raps my kitchen window, eyeballs permafrost to the glass. Wintry satsumas spill from her left hand. Her right fastens a storm-flap, scissors her décolletage. It's been dark ages, she mouths, party-red syrup askew, voice detuned from drink. She charades in fingerless gloves and mimes something about bobsleds and batteries. I lock the door.

With a sledge and two torches, we Rosebud deep drifts, a green plastic pixel skating downhill, westward towards reflected plasma.

REFLEX PRESS

Reflex Press is an independent publisher based in Abingdon, Oxfordshire, committed to publishing bold and innovative books by emerging authors from across the UK and beyond.

Since our inception in 2018, we have published award-winning short story collections, flash fiction anthologies, and novella-length fiction.

www.reflex.press
@reflexfiction